Revision  PEARSON PUBLISHING Guides

GCSE Science

Foundation and Higher Tiers

Ted Lister and Janet Renshaw

Illustrations by Matthew Foster-Smith

GCSE Science

Name...

Address ....

....

....

Dates of exams:

....

....

....

Coursework deadline dates:

....

....

....

Exam board ....

Syllabus number..

Candidate number ....

Centre number ....

Further copies of this publication may be obtained from:

Pearson Publishing
Chesterton Mill, French's Road, Cambridge CB4 3NP
Tel 01223 350555   Fax 01223 356484

Email info@pearson.co.uk   Web site http://www.pearson.co.uk/education/

ISBN: 1 85749 427 X

Published by Pearson Publishing 1997
© Pearson Publishing 1997

Contents

Contents

Patterns of behaviour

Physical Processes

Electricity and magnetism

Forces and motion

Waves

The Earth and beyond

Energy resources and energy transfer

Radioactivity

Answers

Introduction

There is no substitute for reading through your notes or your textbook, but it is often difficult to know how to organise your revision.

This revision guide is designed for you to work with it. We suggest that you first read the content of a page. Then, whenever there is a vertical line, cover the right-hand side with a piece of paper and write your answers on the paper. It doesn't matter if your answers are not the same word for word, as long as you have the right meaning. Most of the diagrams are drawn so that you can cover up the labels and try to fill them in from memory. This is another way to test yourself.

There are also questions within each section which will help you check your progress. Note that the space allotted for completing the sentences is **not** indicative of the length of the missing words. When the spaces are being filled in, care will need to be taken to write neatly, in very small writing. Answers to the questions are provided on pages 175 to 186.

In general, the harder topics which are primarily aimed at A and B candidates are at the end of the section, but if you find a part which is particularly hard, go back to your notes, then try again. Read through to the end of a section for definitions of terms, words or abbreviations used.

Although most of the revision is relevant for all syllabuses, there are differences between syllabuses, so check with your teacher if you are in doubt.

The order in which topics are covered also differs between syllabuses, but this doesn't matter for your final revision.

Good luck!

Life Processes
and Living Things

Life processes and cell activity

Plants and animals are living things. As living things they show or are capable of showing the following life processes:

M	Movement
E	Excretion
R	Respiration
R	Reproduction
I	Irritability
N	Nutrition
G	Growth

Cells

All living material is built of cells. Cells have complicated internal structures and carry out all the chemical reactions which drive the processes of life.

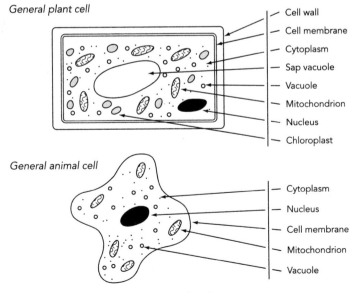

General plant cell

— Cell wall
— Cell membrane
— Cytoplasm
— Sap vacuole
— Vacuole
— Mitochondrion
— Nucleus
— Chloroplast

General animal cell

— Cytoplasm
— Nucleus
— Cell membrane
— Mitochondrion
— Vacuole

Note: The plural of mitochondrion is mitochondria

The parts within the cell are called	organelles.
Both animal and plant cells have	nucleus, cell membrane, cytoplasm, mitochondria.
Plant cells also have	a cell wall, vacuole, chloroplasts.

Main parts of cells	**What they do**
Cell membrane	allows some small molecules, such as glucose, in and out but not larger ones such as starch. It is a **selectively-permeable** membrane.
Nucleus	controls the cell.
Cytoplasm	a watery fluid where many chemical reactions take place under the action of enzymes. It also stores food.
Mitochondria	are the structures in which the reactions of respiration (the energy-releasing process) take place.

Plants only	
Chloroplasts	are tiny structures which contain the green pigment chlorophyll. This is essential for photosynthesis as it absorbs light energy.
Sap vacuoles	contain cell sap and help to support the plant cell.
Cell wall	allows even large molecules through and is therefore fully permeable. It is made of cellulose fibres and is strong enough to protect and support the plant cell.

Ⓠuestion

Complete the following sentences:

Every living organism is made up of .... All cells are surrounded by a

...., are filled with .... and are controlled by a

.... The .... is called .... because it only

allows particles below a certain size to pass through it. Plant cells also have a

.... to protect and support the cell. This is fully ....

They also contain chloroplasts which contain .... This is a green-coloured

chemical that .... light. The .... are full of cell sap.

Specialisation

Some animals, such as amoebae, consist of only one cell, but in more complicated forms of life, cells are specialised within the organism to do different jobs.

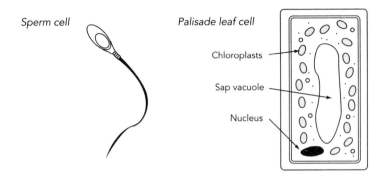

Sperm cell

Palisade leaf cell

Chloroplasts

Sap vacuole

Nucleus

Hint: If you are asked in what ways a particular cell is specialised for its function, look to see how it is different from a typical cell and use your common sense to make a guess if you don't know the answer.

Ⓠuestion

Say how each of the cells – a sperm cell and a palisade leaf cell – (see above) are specialised for its particular use.

Specialised cells collect together to form	tissues.
Different tissues group together to form	organs.
Different organs group together to form	systems.
All the systems make up the	organism.

For example:

Cells	**Tissue**	**Organ**	**System**
Liver cells	▶ Liver tissue	▶ Liver	▶ Digestive system

Organs

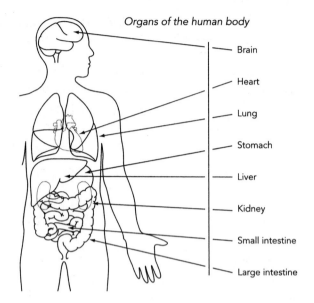

Organs of the human body

- Brain
- Heart
- Lung
- Stomach
- Liver
- Kidney
- Small intestine
- Large intestine

Flowering plant organs

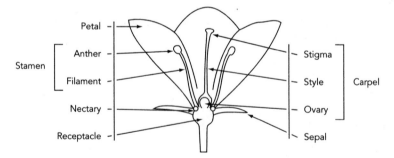

Petal

Stamen
- Anther
- Filament

Nectary

Receptacle

Stigma

Style — Carpel

Ovary

Sepal

Question

For each of the following, say whether it is an organelle, a cell, a tissue, an organ, a system or an organism:

a   Eye   b   Sap vacuole   c   Sperm

d   Buttercup   e   Nucleus   f   Amoeba.

How substances enter and leave the cell

Most cells are bathed in an aqueous (water-based) solution, and gases and some other dissolved substances drift in and out of them by the process of **diffusion**.

The three ways that substances move in and out of cells are	diffusion, osmosis and active transport.
Diffusion is	the random spreading out of substances which distributes them evenly.
This means that substances move	from high concentrations to lower ones.
Diffusion occurs in respiration	when oxygen and carbon dioxide move in and out of cells.
Osmosis is	the diffusion of **water** from a less concentrated (more dilute) solution to a more concentrated one.
Osmosis occurs in cells because	the cell membrane is **selectively- or partially-permeable**.
This means that	some molecules are too large to pass through it.
Active transport is	the movement of substances from a region of low concentration to one of high concentration (the opposite of osmosis and diffusion).
This requires	energy from the cell.

Osmosis

Selectively-permeable membrane

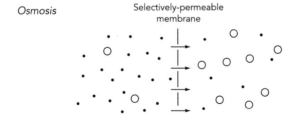

Water molecules • move through the selectively-permeable membrane to equalise the concentration of the larger molecules ○ on both sides

Active transport occurs, for example, in plants when some materials move up the phloem and others move down it and in the contractile vacuole of the amoeba which fills with water even though its contents are more dilute than the cell's cytoplasm.

Questions

1 What is the difference between diffusion and osmosis?

2 Complete the following sentences:

During osmosis, if two solutions are separated by a ....

...................., the water moves .... the more dilute solution ....

the less dilute one. A more dilute solution has .... water than a less

dilute one so in terms of water it is .... concentrated.

> The **membranes** that surround all cells may also be called **partially-permeable** or **semi-permeable** as well as **selectively-permeable** as used above. They all mean the same thing.

Humans as organisms

Nutrition

Studying human nutrition involves looking at our food and the way in which we feed.

Food

A balanced diet requires:	carbohydrates to provide energy
	proteins for growth and cell repair
	fats to provide energy and make cell membranes
	minerals and vitamins for chemical reactions within the body
	fibre to bulk up food.
Digestion is	the process by which food is broken down chemically into small particles which will dissolve and pass into the bloodstream.
The chemical reactions by which food is broken down are catalysed (sped up) by	enzymes.
Enzymes are	proteins which speed up specific chemical reactions.

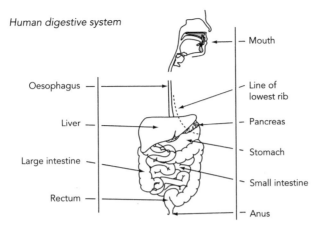

Human digestive system

- Mouth
- Line of lowest rib
- Pancreas
- Stomach
- Small intestine
- Anus

Oesophagus —
Liver —
Large intestine —
Rectum —

Stages of digestion

1 **In the mouth**

Teeth break up the food:

molars and premolars	grind food
incisors	slice through food
canines	grip food helping to tear it into smaller pieces.
Saliva	lubricates the food.
Saliva contains the enzyme	salivary amylase which converts starch into maltose. This is the first stage of the chemical breakdown of food.
Saliva also helps	to keep the teeth clean.
The food passes down the	oesophagus.
It moves along by the process of	peristalsis.

2 **In the stomach**

	chemical digestion continues.
Gastric juice contains:	proteases, enzymes which digest protein
	hydrochloric acid which kills off bacteria and provides the correct pH for the enzyme to work best.

3 **In the small intestine**

chemical digestion continues and food is absorbed into the blood stream.

In the duodenum:

bile (made in the liver and stored in the gall bladder)

neutralises some of the acid, emulsifies fats (breaks them down into tiny droplets) making them easier to digest

food is mixed with enzymes from

pancreatic juice which break down carbohydrates, proteins and fats.

In the ileum:

More enzymes

complete the break up of food so that it is soluble and can pass through the wall into the bloodstream.

This process is called

absorption.

Absorption is fast because:

the surface area of the ileum is increased by villi (singular villus)

the lining epithelium is very thin

each villus has a plentiful blood supply

digestion has broken food down into small, water-soluble molecules.

Food passed into the blood-stream goes to the liver via

the hepatic portal vein.

Villus structure

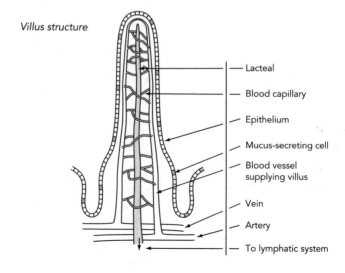

— Lacteal

— Blood capillary

— Epithelium

— Mucus-secreting cell

— Blood vessel supplying villus

— Vein

— Artery

— To lymphatic system

4 **In the large intestine**

food which can't be digested passes into the colon and rectum where it is egested (expelled).

water and salt are absorbed in the colon as required.

waste food passes out of the body through the anus (defaecation).

The lining of the gut or alimentary canal secretes mucus which

lubricates the passage of the food and protects the alimentary canal from being digested.

Enzyme action

Carbohydrates such as starch are converted to

simple sugars (such as glucose) by amylase.

This happens in

the mouth and small intestine.

Proteins are converted to

amino acids by proteases.

This happens in the

stomach and small intestine.

Fats are converted to

fatty acids and glycerol by lipase.

This happens in the

small intestine.

Food tests

The test for starch is

iodine solution turns from yellow/brown to blue-black.

The test for protein is

biuret solution turns from blue to violet.

The test for fat is

grease-proof paper is marked by a fat.

The test for a simple sugar is

Benedict's solution turns from blue to brick-red when warmed.

Questions

1 a   What are enzymes?

   b   Why are they so important to digestion?

   c   Describe how they act on the three main food groups.

2   Complete the following sentences:

The digestive canal can be thought of as a long muscular ....

Ingestion is the process of .... in food. Digestion is the process of

.... it down so that it can pass through finger-like folds called

.... which are found in the .... , a part of the ....

intestine. Undigested food passes on to the .... intestine, which is

divided into the .... and the .... Here .... and

.... are reabsorbed. Finally, faeces are passed out from the anus. This is

called ....

Circulation

Blood circulates throughout the body in a system of tubes or vessels. It is kept
moving by the heart and delivers food and oxygen to the cells and removes carbon
dioxide and other waste.

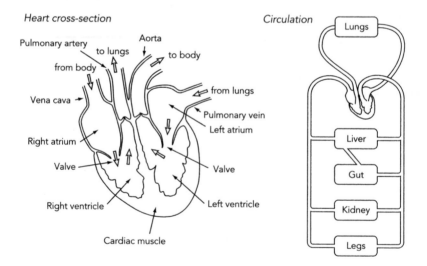

The heart is	a muscular double pump.
It is divided into	four chambers.
The two atria receive blood from	the veins.
The two ventricles receive blood from	the atria.

The left ventricle pumps blood to	the whole body, delivering oxygen.
The right ventricle pumps blood to	the lungs to collect oxygen and deposit carbon dioxide.

> **Hint:** Remember that in a diagram of the heart the **left** atrium and **left** ventricle are on the **right-hand** side of the paper.

ⓠuestions

1   What kind of muscle is the heart made from?

2   Why do the ventricles have more muscular walls than the atria?

3   Which ventricle of the heart is thicker and why?

4   In the circulation diagram on page 10, colour in the oxygenated blood red, and the deoxygenated blood blue. Label the veins and arteries.

5   What is the function of the heart valves?

Veins, arteries and capillaries

Blood circulates through these main types of vessels – veins, arteries and capillaries.

Arteries

The walls of arteries are	relatively thick and elastic.
This is because	they carry oxygenated blood from the heart to different parts of the body.
The blood is	at a high pressure.
An exception to this is the	pulmonary artery
This carries deoxygenated blood	from the heart.

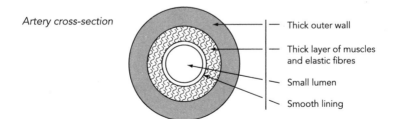

Artery cross-section

— Thick outer wall

— Thick layer of muscles and elastic fibres

— Small lumen

— Smooth lining

11

Veins

Compared with arteries:

The blood is	at a lower pressure.
The walls of veins are	thinner.
The diameter of veins is	larger.
Veins have valves to	stop the blood flowing backwards.
They carry blood	to the heart.
An exception to this is the	hepatic portal vein which takes blood from the intestine to the liver.

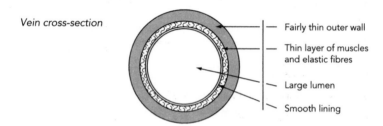

Vein cross-section

— Fairly thin outer wall

— Thin layer of muscles and elastic fibres

— Large lumen

— Smooth lining

Capillaries

A capillary network

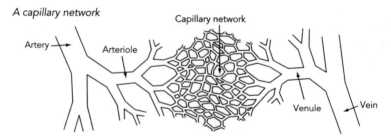

Artery

Arteriole

Capillary network

Venule

Vein

Capillaries are formed by the division of arteries (and veins) into smaller and smaller vessels.

The walls are	very thin (often one cell thick).
They leak	tissue fluid.
This is where	food and oxygen pass into the body's cells and waste products such as carbon dioxide pass out.

Ⓠuestions

1 Complete the following sentences:

Arteries have strong walls because they carry high pressure, ... blood

round the body. .... is needed for respiration. The veins carry

.... blood back to the .... atrium of the heart which pumps it

into the .... ventricle. From there it goes to the ....

Blood is prevented from flowing backwards in veins by .... Blood is

also kept moving in veins by the .... round them which squeeze the

veins. The third sort of blood vessels, ... , are very thin because

.... and .... must be able to diffuse quickly

through their walls into the cells.

2 a What are capillaries and what are they for?

 b What are the benefits of having capillaries that are:
   i   branched
   ii very thin-walled
   iii narrow?

Blood

Composition

The four main components of blood are:

plasma
red blood cells
white blood cells
platelets.

Blood cells

Red blood cell	Platelets	Two types of white blood cell	

Doughnut-shaped   Lymphocyte, with   Phagocyte with
                         large nucleus   lobed nucleus, which
                                           can engulf bacteria

Blood cells	Description	Function

Plasma	• Straw-coloured watery solution of dissolved:
	  – food broken down by digestion
	  – minerals
	  – carbon dioxide
	  – urea
	  – hormones
		• The carrier of all the substances that make up blood
		• Transports heat round the body

Red blood cells	• Contain haemoglobin • Mature ones have no nucleus	• Carry oxygen as oxyhaemoglobin. • In areas of low oxygen, give up oxygen and combine with carbon dioxide
White blood cells	• Variable shapes, contain a nucleus	• Engulf and destroy harmful bacteria • Make antibodies • Produce antitoxins which neutralise the toxins (poisons) produced by bacteria
Platelets	• Small particles with no nucleus	• Involved in the process of clotting

Questions

1 List the functions of blood as:

  a a transport system

  b as a defence system against harmful microbes.

2 Complete the following sentences:

Red blood cells are made in the .... of some bones. A mature red cell has

no .... It contains the pigment .... which is a protein-based

molecule. This pigment is coloured .... and contains .... When

combined with oxygen it is called .... and is bright red in colour. This is

why there is difference in .... between .... and venous blood.

.... blood is bright red, whereas venous blood is ....

....

Gas exchange and respiration

Gas exchange takes place in the lungs – oxygen is taken up and carbon dioxide removed. Respiration is a chemical process which takes place in all cells.

Breathing

This is the physical process which draws air into and out of the lungs.

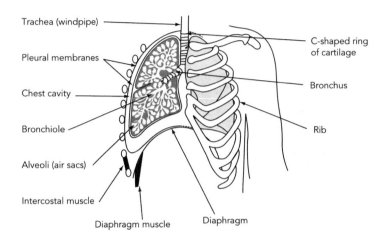

Trachea (windpipe)

C-shaped ring of cartilage

Pleural membranes

Chest cavity

Bronchus

Bronchiole

Rib

Alveoli (air sacs)

Intercostal muscle

Diaphragm muscle

Diaphragm

We breathe in to	obtain oxygen from the air.
When we breathe in our ribs	lift up.
At the same time our diaphragm is	lowered (pulled down).
The volume of air in the lungs is	increased.
The pressure in the lungs is	decreased.
Air rushes in through	our mouth (or nose) to even out the pressure.
The breathing passages are	moist and warm.
They have along their lengths tiny 'hairs' called	cilia.
These have the job of	keeping the lungs clean.
Air enters the lungs through	the trachea (or windpipe).
This branches into two	bronchi (singular bronchus).
These branch into many	bronchioles (singular bronchiole).

At the end of these are the	alveoli (singular alveolus) or air sacs.
These have the following properties:	a large, moist, surface area a good blood supply are very thin (only one cell thick).
These properties mean that	gases are able to diffuse quickly between the blood and the lungs.

Gas exchange in an alveolus

Deoxygenated blood enters alveolus

Alveolus wall

Air entering and leaving

Oxygenated blood leaves alveolus

Blood capillary wall

Red blood cell

Diffusion of carbon dioxide (out of blood)

Moisture

Plasma

Diffusion of oxygen (into blood)

The composition of inhaled and exhaled air

Inhaled air is air that	enters the lungs.
It is made up approximately of:	21% oxygen 0.03% carbon dioxide 79% nitrogen and other gases.
Exhaled air is air that	leaves the lungs.
It is made up of approximately of:	16% oxygen 4% carbon dioxide 79% nitrogen and other gases.
The difference is because	during respiration oxygen is used up and carbon dioxide is given out.

Smoking: Tobacco smoke contains tar which deposits in the lungs. This may limit the capacity of the lungs and cause bronchial problems or may lead to cancer. Smoking produces the gas carbon monoxide which replaces oxygen in oxyhaemoglobin and reduces the capacity of the blood to carry oxygen.

Respiration

Respiration is the process by which	cells release energy from food.
Aerobic respiration uses the gas	oxygen.
The word equation is	glucose + oxygen $\longrightarrow$ carbon dioxide + water [+ energy]
The symbol equation is	$C_6H_{12}O_6 + 6O_2 \longrightarrow 6CO_2 + 6H_2O$ [+ energy]
Aerobic respiration is carried out in the	mitochondria of cells.

Hint: Don't muddle respiration and breathing. All living material respires to transfer energy from food. Breathing is the mechanism by which some animals obtain their oxygen for respiration and remove carbon dioxide, the waste product.

Anaerobic respiration is respiration without	oxygen.
A microbe which may respire anaerobically is	yeast.
The word equation is	glucose $\longrightarrow$ alcohol + carbon dioxide [+ energy]
This is called	fermentation.
We respire anaerobically when	we exercise to the point where our muscles cannot get enough oxygen for aerobic respiration.
Respiring anaerobically can lead to an	oxygen debt.
This debt must be	'repaid' when exercise is over.
The word equation is	glucose $\longrightarrow$ lactic acid [+ energy]
The presence of lactic acid may cause	muscle pain.
Anaerobic respiration produces less energy than	aerobic respiration.

ⓠuestions

1 Give at least three features that an efficient respiratory surface has and explain why it has them.

2 How are aerobic and anaerobic respiration alike and how do they differ?

3 Complete the following sentences:

The process by which .... passes into the blood and ....

.... passes out of the blood is called gas .... Gases pass

across a .... surface. Oxygen is used by the cells for .... We

draw air into our lungs by .... During .... , the diaphragm

moves down and the rib cage moves upwards and outwards. This ....

the volume of the thorax and air is drawn into the ....

The nervous system

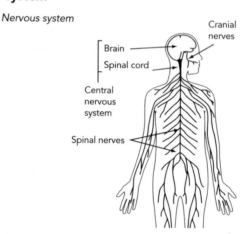

Nervous system

Brain

Spinal cord

Central nervous system

Spinal nerves

Cranial nerves

Organisms need to be able to detect changes in their environment.

These changes are called	stimuli.
The parts of the organism that detect stimuli are called	receptors.
Detecting a stimulus can bring about	a response.
This is carried out via an	effector (eg muscles in animals).
Reacting to a response is called	behaviour.

Animals need fast communication between the receptors and effectors.
Nerves are made up of specialised cells which pass messages very quickly.

Messages are transmitted as	electrical impulses.
Nerve cells are called	neurones.
Junctions between neurones are called	synapses.
The relay neurones are found in	the central nervous system.
The central nervous system (CNS) is made up of	the brain and the spinal cord.
The job of the central nervous system is to	process stimuli it receives and organise reactions.

Neurone (nerve cell)

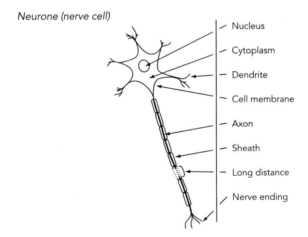

Nucleus

Cytoplasm

Dendrite

Cell membrane

Axon

Sheath

Long distance

Nerve ending

Stimulus and response

The usual way that a message is acted upon is:

Sensory receptor
  ⟶ Sensory neurone
    ⟶ CNS (brain)
      ⟶ Motor neurone
        ⟶ Effector

Chemicals released at the synapses carry the impulse across the gap.

Examples of stimuli and receptor organs are:

Sense	Receptors
Balance	Eye and ear
Sound	Ear
Light	Eye
Airborne chemicals	Nose
Water-borne chemicals	Tongue
Heat and cold	Skin
Pin-prick	Skin

Reflex action

A reflex action is an immediate response to a stimulus. It is very fast as it is first dealt with by the spinal cord and so bypasses the brain. The message will also be sent to the brain but the reaction will have happened by the time the brain receives it.

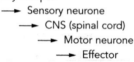

Sensory receptor
→ Sensory neurone
→ CNS (spinal cord)
→ Motor neurone
→ Effector

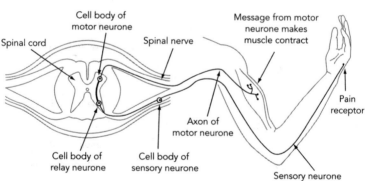

Cell body of motor neurone

Spinal cord

Spinal nerve

Message from motor neurone makes muscle contract

Axon of motor neurone

Pain receptor

Cell body of relay neurone

Cell body of sensory neurone

Sensory neurone

Questions

1 a How are neurones similar to other animal cells?

   b How are they adapted to their function?

2 a Explain how the reflex arc works and why it is important.

   b Give an example of a reflex arc in action.

   c When you hurt yourself, why is the pain sometimes felt after you have taken action to prevent the pain?

The eye

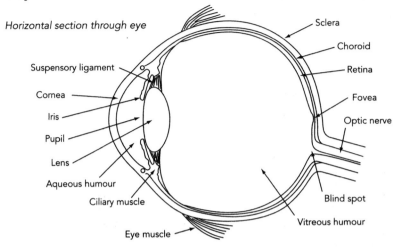

Horizontal section through eye

Suspensory ligament

Cornea

Iris

Pupil

Lens

Aqueous humour

Ciliary muscle

Eye muscle

Sclera

Choroid

Retina

Fovea

Optic nerve

Blind spot

Vitreous humour

How the parts of the eye function

The sclera	surrounds the eye and protects it.
The cornea	bends the light that enters the eye.
The iris	changes size to control the amount of light entering the eye.
The pupil is	the hole in the middle of the iris.
The lens focuses light onto the retina by	changing shape.
The ciliary muscles	change the shape of the lens.
The suspensory ligaments	support the lens.
The retina	collects light stimuli with its receptor cells.
The rods and cones are	light sensitive cells on the retina.
The rods work best in	dim light.
The cones detect	colour and detail.
The choroid layer	is a black layer behind the retina which absorbs light.
The blind spot is	the area where the optic nerve leaves the retina.
The optic nerve	transmits images to the brain.
The eyeball is moved by	sets of eye muscles.

Light and the eye

The amount of light entering the eye depends on	the iris.
This controls the size of the	pupil.

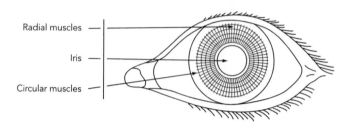

When the circular muscles contract, the pupil is	smaller.
When the radial muscles contract the pupil is	larger.

Eye relaxed (focused on a distant object)

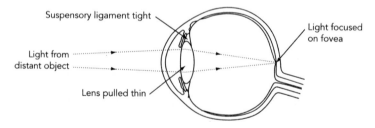

Eye focused on near object

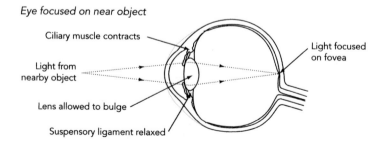

Light rays are focused by	the cornea and lens.
When the rays of light are coming from a close up object the lens is	bulging.
When the rays of light are coming from far away the lens is	flat.
Light rays must be focused onto	the retina.
The fovea is	the most sensitive spot on the retina.

Questions

1 Complete the following sentences:

The iris has two sets of muscles, the .... and .... When the .... contract, the radials are relaxed and the .... gets smaller in size so that .... light enters the eye. When the the radials contract, the circular muscles are .... and the pupil is .... in size so that more .... enters the eye.

2 a Explain how light from a distant object is focused onto the retina.

b Explain the difference when the object is close up.

3 Complete the following sentences:

The lens of the eye is held in place by .... muscles. When these contract, the suspensory ligaments which encircle the lens, are pulled tight. These pull the lens to a .... shape. When the muscles are .... , the .... slacken and the .... bulges.

Hormones

The other way (apart from the nervous system) that messages are carried round the body is by special chemicals called hormones. They circulate in the blood and their action is slower than that of the nervous system.

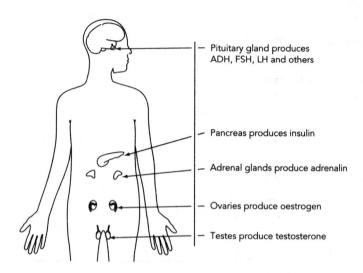

Pituitary gland produces ADH, FSH, LH and others

Pancreas produces insulin

Adrenal glands produce adrenalin

Ovaries produce oestrogen

Testes produce testosterone

A hormone is a	chemical messenger.
Hormones are produced by	glands.
They are carried round the body in the	bloodstream.
A hormone affects a specific organ called	the target organ.

How insulin controls the level of blood sugar

Eating a meal containing carbohydrate causes	blood sugar to rise.
The pancreas responds by	secreting insulin.
This causes the liver and muscles to	take up glucose and store it as glycogen.
The blood sugar level	falls.
The pancreas	stops secreting insulin.
The liver and muscles	convert glycogen to glucose.

Someone who does not produce enough insulin has	diabetes.
This disease can be treated by	daily insulin injections (or diet if mild).
The three things that must be balanced are	carbohydrate intake, exercise and insulin.
If the insulin level is too high this must be corrected with	sugar intake.

How the sex hormones do their work

The pituitary gland starts the process of puberty by producing a hormone which starts the ovaries and testes producing their hormones.

The time of when people become sexually mature is called	puberty.
The hormone mainly responsible for puberty in females is	oestrogen.
The hormone mainly responsible for puberty in males is	testosterone.
The body changes that occur in females are	menstruation, development of breasts, widening of the hip girdle, body hair.
Menstruation means that	mature eggs are being released from the ovaries.
The body changes that occur in males are	body becomes more muscular, facial and body hair appear, voice deepens, sperm becomes mature.

The menstrual cycle

From puberty until middle age, the female reproductive system goes through a regular monthly, hormone-controlled sequence of events called the menstrual cycle.

The two main hormones active in this process are	oestrogen and progesterone.
The hormone that starts the thickening of the uterus lining is	oestrogen.
The hormone that maintains the uterus lining is	progesterone.

Steps in the cycle (only the points in bold type are required by most boards – check with your teacher)

FSH stands for	follicle stimulating hormone.
FSH is secreted by the	pituitary gland and starts the menstrual cycle off.
A follicle (containing **an egg**) **ripens in the**	**ovary.**
The follicle in **the ovary releases oestrogens and**	**the lining of the womb gradually thickens.**
The oestrogens inhibit the production of	FSH.
They stimulate the production of	LH (luteinising hormone) from the pituitary.
LH stimulates **the release of the egg** in the follicle which **is called**	**ovulation.**
The follicle becomes	a corpus luteum (yellow body).
The corpus luteum in **the ovary stops releasing oestrogen and produces**	**progesterone.**
The egg passes along	**the fallopian tube.**
The egg dies within 48 hours if	**it is not fertilised.**
The corpus luteum in the ovary no longer produces	**progesterone.**
The lining of the uterus	**breaks down and is expelled.**
This is called	**menstruation.**
This cycle occurs every	**month.**

> If fertilisation takes place, the corpus luteum continues to produce progesterone and so does the placenta, which then supports a developing baby.

Question

What do A, B, C and D represent in this diagram of the menstrual cycle?

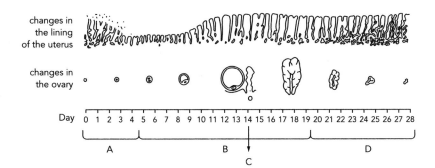

changes in the lining of the uterus

changes in the ovary

Day 0 1 2 3 4 5 6 7 8 9 10 11 12 13 14 15 16 17 18 19 20 21 22 23 24 25 26 27 28

A   B   C   D

Hormones and fertility

The standard contraceptive pill contains	oestrogen and progesterone.
In suitable dosages these stop	ovulation.
Oestrogen inhibits the production of	FSH.
This means that	the eggs do not mature.

Hormones can also be supplied to women who are not ovulating, to promote ovulation. This is one type of fertility treatment. FSH is the fertility drug given to women to stimulate eggs to mature.

Adrenalin

The effects of adrenalin are designed to	prepare us for immediate action in response to danger.
The heart beats faster so that	more oxygen is supplied to the brain and the muscles.
The blood vessels in the skin and gut contract so that	more blood goes to the brain and muscles.

Homeostasis

This is the process that	keeps the body in a steady state.
Some examples include controlling:	the water content of the body the level of blood sugar the ion content of the body the temperature of the body.
The temperature of the body is kept constant by the action of	the skin.
Blood sugar levels are kept constant by the action of	insulin.
Water and salt content is kept in balance by the	kidney and ADH.
Body fluids (including blood) are at	a constant concentration.
If a blood cell is added to a solution of a higher concentration	water from the blood cell passes out of the cell and the cell shrinks.
If a blood cell is added to a solution that is more dilute than it is	water enters the cell and it will eventually burst.
This is the process of	osmosis.

Hint: A fluid which has the same concentration as blood is said to be **isotonic** to blood.

Ⓠuestion

Complete the following sentences:

The level of blood sugar is controlled by .... This is released by the

.... whenever the blood glucose level .... Under its effect the

.... and muscles store sugar as .... Some people do not make

enough of this hormone. They have the disease .... This can have two

effects, both of which are harmful:

a   After a meal containing .... , the blood may contain far too much ....

b   The muscles and liver will not build up stores of .... , so when the blood

    glucose level drops there are no reserves. This means the blood glucose level

    could become dangerously ....

Removal of waste products

Many waste products become poisonous if they accumulate so they must be removed.

The main waste product of respiration is	carbon dioxide.
This is eliminated from the body via	the lungs.
The main waste product from digestion is	urea.
This is formed in the	liver.
This is eliminated from the body via the	kidneys.

The kidneys

The kidneys help control water and salt balance and the removal of urea. They form part of the urinary system.

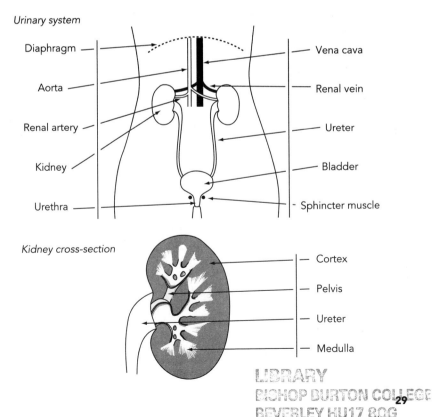

Urinary system

Diaphragm — Vena cava
Aorta — Renal vein
Renal artery — Ureter
Kidney — Bladder
Urethra — Sphincter muscle

Kidney cross-section

Cortex
Pelvis
Ureter
Medulla

How the kidney works

The functional unit of the kidney is a long, very fine tube called a nephron. Each kidney has several million nephrons.

The nephron in action

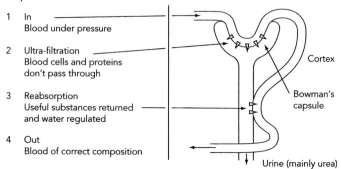

1 In
   Blood under pressure

2 Ultra-filtration
   Blood cells and proteins
   don't pass through

3 Reabsorption
   Useful substances returned
   and water regulated

4 Out
   Blood of correct composition

Cortex

Bowman's
capsule

Urine (mainly urea)

Blood enters the kidney under pressure via	the renal artery.
It is filtered into the nephron at	the Bowman's capsule.
The large particles which do not pass into the kidney include	blood cells and protein molecules.
The small particles which do pass through are	water, glucose, amino acids, vitamins, urea and ions.
The useful substances (some water, glucose, amino acids, vitamins and some ions) are	reabsorbed back into the bloodstream.
In the kidney stay	urea, unwanted ions and excess water.
This mixture is passed out from the body via the bladder as	urine.

> **Dialysis:** Many people whose kidneys do not work properly are kept alive by dialysis. The urea from the patient's blood is drawn off as it passes through a dialysis machine. The blood is separated by a selectively-permeable membrane from a solution containing no urea, so the urea passes into the solution.

Controlling water content

We lose water all the time by: | breathing out
sweating
urination
expelling faeces.

We gain water by: | drinking
eating
respiration (this produces carbon
dioxide and water in the cells).

Hormone control

The hormone that controls the
water level in our blood is | ADH.

This stands for | anti-diuretic hormone.

It is released from the | pituitary gland.

If the water content of the
blood is too low | ADH is released.

This causes | the kidneys to reabsorb more
water from urine.

The urine becomes | more concentrated and lower in volume.

If the water content of the
blood is too high | ADH is not released.

This causes | less water to be reabsorbed
by the kidney.

The urine is | more dilute and higher in volume.

Hint: ADH **A**dds water to the blood.

Ⓠuestions

1   "The kidney works by filtration and reabsorption." Explain carefully how this is so.

2   Complete the following sentences:

The kidneys are part of the .... system. The renal .... brings

blood to the kidneys. The job of the kidney is to take unwanted substances from

the .... A kidney has three main parts – the cortex, the ....

and the pelvis. A tube called the .... leads from the .... This

tube carries .... to the .... The renal .... carries

processed blood from the kidney.

Body temperature

Maintaining a constant, relatively high body temparature is particularly important because our body chemistry relies on enzymes (biological catalysts) and these work best at a particular temperature (about 37°C).

Raising the body temperature

This is done by:

shivering because	jerky muscle movements generate heat from the process of respiration
constriction of blood vessels because	the blood vessels supplying the skin capillaries narrow to prevent heat loss
hair erector muscles contracting to make hair stand on end because	this traps warm air.

Losing heat from the body

This is done by:

sweating because	sweat evaporates from the skin removing heat from the body
vasodilation because	the blood vessels supplying skin capillaries enlarge and heat is lost from the blood at the skin surface.

How is temperature controlled?

A centre in the brain called the thermoregulatory centre contains receptors which are sensitive to the temperature of the blood flowing through the brain. Receptors in the skin send impulses to this centre and impulses are sent back to the relevant effectors.

❶uestions

1   Put in the following labels in the correct position: Hair follicle, Sebaceous gland, Dead cells, Sweat gland, Erector muscle.

Skin cross-section

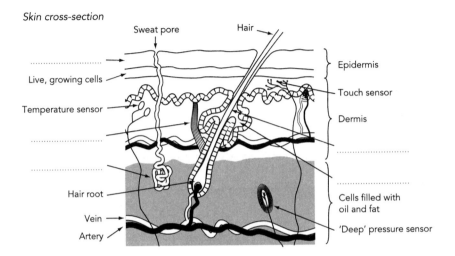

2   Why do we get hot after vigorous exercise?

3   Why is it more difficult to cool down in a humid atmosphere than in a dry one?

4   Why do several thin layers of clothing keep us warmer than a single thick layer of the same kind of material?

5   Complete the following sentences:

The skin is an important organ in regulating the .... of our bodies. It

contains .... glands which release a watery liquid. This evaporates at the

surface using heat from the .... and thus cools us. Also tiny blood

.... run just under the surface of the skin. These .... when we

are hot and radiate .... from the body. When mammals are cold, the

hair erector muscles .... and their hair stands up. This traps ....

under the hairs and keeps them warm. Under the surface of the skin is a layer of

.... This acts as an ....

Feedback

Keeping the body in a steady state is managed automatically by the brain in a continuous monitoring process. When the body becomes out of balance (eg too much water or too much sugar in the blood) the brain sends out nervous impulses or hormones to make any corrections that are needed. Once the correct state is reached, other nervous impulses or a further hormone may be sent out to halt the effect of the first. This correcting mechanism is called **negative feedback**.

Health

We are surrounded by microbes in the air and some of these are harmful. Dust and germs in the air are breathed in continually.

We may also take in bacteria and viruses with our food. We may be infected via another organism, eg mosquitos carry the parasite that causes malaria.

Our bodies have a series of defence mechanisms to counter these threats of infection.

The first line of defence

Our skin forms	a tough, waterproof barrier.
It produces an oily substance called	sebum.
Sebum is produced by	the sebaceous glands.
It has the properties of being	water repellent and mildly antiseptic.
Dust and germs do not usually reach the lungs because	a sticky mucus covers the walls of the nasal passages, windpipe and lungs.
Once in the respiratory tract, they are moved along by	fine hair-like filaments called cilia.
These may waft the debris	into the throat.
If germs are swallowed in food or drink (or following the action of cilia) many are killed in the stomach by the action of	stomach acid and digestive enzymes.
Tears protect our eyes because	they contain a substance, called lysozyme, which destroys many microbes.

The next line of defence

Skin

If the skin is damaged	bleeding occurs.
This has the effect of	washing the wound.
The bleeding stops and the wound is closed by the process of	clotting.
Clots are formed from	platelets and damaged tissue which turn a blood protein into fibrin and make a tangled network of fibres.

The white cells in the blood

There are	three sorts of white cells.
When harmful microbes first enter the blood they are engulfed by	phagocytes.
If this doesn't work	lymphocytes produce antibodies.
Once we have recovered from a disease, the ability to produce antibodies rapidly provides	immunity to that disease.
After a bacterial invasion, white cells may produce	antitoxins.
These neutralise	the toxins caused by bacteria.

White cells are not only part of blood: if bacteria escape into the lymphatic system, white cells in the liver, spleen or lymph nodes will attack them.

Drugs and the body

A drug is	any substance that changes the body chemistry.
Analgesics are	pain killers.
Examples include	aspirin and paracetamol.
Antibiotics	kill bacteria
An example is	penicillin.
Depressants	slow down the body chemistry.
An example is	alcohol.
Stimulants	speed up the body chemistry.
An example is	caffeine.

Some drugs are addictive and can also have harmful side effects.

Some harmful side effects of commonly-used drugs

Tobacco contains	nicotine, a very addictive drug.
Tobacco smoke may cause:	lung cancer other lung problems such as emphysema disease of the heart and blood vessels.
Alcohol:	can be addictive slows down reactions and affects judgement may cause damage to the liver.
Solvents:	affect behaviour may cause damage to the lungs, liver, brain and kidneys.

Nobody yet knows all the possible damage that long-term use of other recreational drugs may cause, though there is now increasing evidence that there are real hazards to many of them.

Questions

1   Give an outline of how the body defends itself when a pathogen (harmful microbe) enters the body through a cut in the skin and produces a disease.

2   Complete the following sentences:

One reason that tobacco smoke is harmful over a long period is that it contains carcinogens and the likelihood of getting lung .... increases. But other effects also cause damage. For example, the tar damages .... so that the lungs become less efficient at getting rid of debris. This can lead to .... , a disease that fills the bronchioles with fluid, and even emphysema, where the lungs are choked up. All these diseases mean that there is less space for gas exchange to take place and the body gets starved of .... Any vigorous activity becomes impossible. So why do so many people smoke? The answer is that tobacco contains the drug .... which is highly .... The general pattern is that we start smoking when we are .... and try to give it up as we get ....

Green plants as organisms

Photosynthesis

Plants, unlike animals, can make their own food.

Photosynthesis is	the process by which green plants make their food.
They build up sugars from	carbon dioxide and water.
Photosynthesis takes place within the	leaves.
Energy for photosynthesis is absorbed in the form of	light.
Light is absorbed by the chemical	chlorophyll.
This is found within cells in the organelles called	chloroplasts.
The word equation for photosynthesis is	energy from sunlight absorbed by chlorophyll carbon dioxide + water $\longrightarrow$ glucose + oxygen
The balanced symbol equation is	$6CO_2 + 6H_2O \longrightarrow C_6H_{12}O_6 + 6O_2$

Leaf structure and function

Structure of a leaf in cross-section

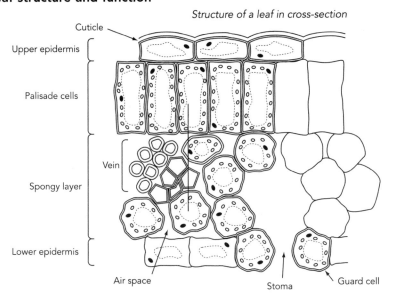

Cuticle

Upper epidermis

Palisade cells

Vein

Spongy layer

Lower epidermis

Air space

Stoma

Guard cell

Leaves are thin and flat to provide	a large surface area.
Most of the photosynthesis takes place in	the palisade cells.
They contain the most	chlorophyll.
Guard cells control	the movement of gases in and out of the stomata.
The leaf vein consists of	phloem and xylem tubes.
Phloem tubes transport	food made by the plant.
Xylem vessels transport	water.
The rate of photosynthesis depends on:	carbon dioxide concentration light intensity light wavelength (colour) temperature availability of water.

Limiting factors: Each of these factors can act as a limiting factor to increasing the rate of photosynthesis. For example, if the carbon dioxide concentration is increased, the rate of photosynthesis will also increase, but only as long as there is enough light available. The availability of light may then become the limiting factor.

Questions

1   Why do leaves usually have a large surface area? Give two reasons.

2   Why do the epidermal cells have no chloroplasts?

How the plant uses the products of photosynthesis

The products of photosynthesis are	glucose and oxygen.
Glucose and oxygen are used for	respiration to produce energy.
Glucose is converted to:	starch (and stored in roots, leaves and stems)
	sucrose (and stored in fruits)
	lipids for storing in seeds
	cellulose for making cell walls
	amino acids to make proteins for growth.

Differences between photosynthesis and respiration

Respiration

glucose + oxygen ⟶	carbon dioxide + water [+ energy]

Photosynthesis

carbon dioxide + water ⟶	glucose + oxygen

Photosynthesis occurs	during daylight.
Respiration occurs	all the time.

> **Remember** that, like animals, plants respire all the time. Unlike animals, when light, carbon dioxide and water are available they photosynthesise.

Ⓠuestions

1 Why do plants not need to expend as much energy as animals?

2 What do plants need energy for and how do they get it?

3 How do plants obtain oxygen?

4 Complete the following sentences:

Plants make their own food by .... They take in .... and

.... and form .... and .... (which

diffuses out of the leaves). This only happens in the presence of ....

usually during daytime, because the process uses .... energy. But

.... goes on all the time and this releases .... and ....

.... In the daytime .... is going on much faster than

.... and the end result is that plants give out .... to the air,

while using all the .... produced during respiration. In the

dark, only .... takes place so plants use .... and give out

....

Minerals needed for healthy growth

For protein synthesis plants need	nitrogen.
For chlorophyll formation plants need	magnesium and iron.
Minerals are absorbed	from the soil through root hairs by active transport.

Phosphorus is needed for enzyme activity and potassium for respiration and photosynthesis, as well as traces of other elements.

Water and transport through the plant

Water is also needed to	support the plant tissues.
Without enough water a plant cell becomes	flaccid.
With enough water a plant cell is	turgid.
If water is withheld, the plant cell dies because of	plasmolysis.

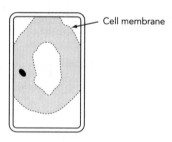

Cell membrane

A turgid cell with swelling sap vacuole	A plasmolysed cell where the vacuole has shrunk due to water loss

Transport through the plant

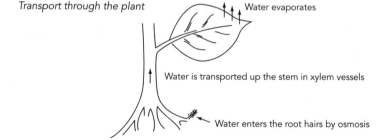

Water evaporates

Water is transported up the stem in xylem vessels

Water enters the root hairs by osmosis

Transpiration

This is the evaporation of water from a plant. The faster the plant transpires, the faster the water is pulled in from the roots.

Transpiration takes place mostly from	the leaves.
Water is lost from	the stomata (singular stoma).
These are found	on the underside of the leaf.
Each stoma or pore is surrounded by a pair of	guard cells.
During dry periods the guard cells become	flaccid.
They therefore	close.
This has the effect of	slowing water loss.

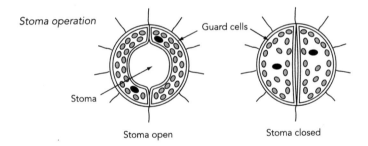

Stoma operation   Guard cells

Stoma

Stoma open   Stoma closed

Transpiration is effected by:	light wind temperature humidity.

Question

For each of the following say how it would affect the rate of transpiration if it were increased. Explain your answer:

a   light

b   wind

c   temperature

d   humidity.

Plant hormones

Plant growth and development is regulated by hormones. Plants have no nervous system but respond to stimuli, using hormones to carry messages.

The main plant stimuli are	light and gravity.
Plants respond to stimuli by	growing in a particular direction.
Responding to light is called	phototropism.
The shoot of a plant grows towards	light (positive phototropism).
Responding to gravity is called	geotropism.
The shoot of a plant grows away from	the pull of gravity (negative geotropism).
One important group of plant growth hormones is	auxins.
Auxins are made	in the tip of the shoot.
Auxins make	the cells just behind the tip grow.
The more auxins	the faster they grow.
Auxins inhibit the growth of	side shoots.

How auxins work

If light shines on a plant from one side, auxins concentrate on the shady side of the tip. This makes the cells grow faster on the shady side and the tip will thus bend towards the light. The cells on the shady side both multiply in number and elongate in shape.

Phototropism

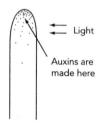

Auxins made in the tip diffuse unevenly down the shoot, concentrating on the shady side

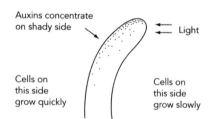

The uneven concentration of auxins causes the shady side to grow faster than the light side, so the shoot bends towards the light

> Some other stimuli which plants may react to are: water, touch and certain chemicals.

Commercial applications of hormones

These include:

the use of rooting hormones on cuttings to promote root growth

killing weeds by disrupting their normal growth pattern

stimulating fruit growth.

Questions

1 What is a tropism?

2 How do tropisms benefit plants? Give examples.

Variation, inheritance and evolution

Variation

Variation is the differences between individual organisms of the same species. It may arise from genetic or environmental causes, such as good or poor diet.

Inheritance

Parents pass certain characteristics on to their children. Children are said to inherit these characteristics. For example, these may include the shape of their ears or nose but not scars or knowledge of science.

Evolution

Organisms live where they are best able to survive. Over time, this has led to the most successfully adapted organism being the survivor. Gradual changes can, over time, lead to new species being produced – evolution (see page 51).

Grouping organisms

Animals

Animals can be divided into

vertebrates and invertebrates.

Vertebrates have

backbones.

Vertebrates can be grouped as

fish, reptiles, amphibians, birds, mammals.

The main external features of each group are:

fish	have scales and gills, live in water, swim using fins.
amphibians	have a smooth moist skin.
reptiles	have a dry scaly skin.
birds	have feathers and wings.
mammals	have a hairy skin. Females suckle their young from mammary glands.
Invertebrates can be divided into the groups	coelenterates (jelly fish), flatworms, true worms, arthropods, molluscs (snails), echinoderms (starfish).
Insects and spiders belong to the group	arthropods.
Insects have	six legs, wings and three sections to their bodies.
The three regions are	head, thorax and abdomen.
The head has	eyes, mouth and antennae.
The thorax has	the legs and wings attached to it.
Spiders have	eight legs and no antennae.

Plants

Plants have two main groups	flowering and non-flowering plants.
The flowering plants consist of	monocotyledons (one seed leaf) and dicotyledons (two seed leaves).
The non-flowering plants consist of	mosses, ferns and conifers.

Question

Say whether the the variation in each the following might be caused by genetics, environment or both:

a   eye colour

b   height

c   life span

d   natural hair colour

e   the language a person speaks.

> **Continuous and discontinuous variation:** Variation may be continuous or discontinuous. For example, factors like height and weight are continuous because they have a smooth spread of values in a population. Factors such as gender (male or female), or the ability to roll the tongue, are discontinuous. A person is either male or female and either can or cannot roll their tongue.

The nature of genetic material

The cell nucleus contains	chromosomes.
A normal human cell contains	23 pairs of chromosomes (totalling 46).
Chromosomes are made up of	genes.
Genes are made of the material	DNA (deoxyribonucleic acid).
Each pair of genes controls	a particular characteristic.

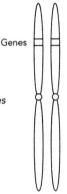

Genes

A pair of
chromosomes

DNA

DNA is a very long
molecule made of
two connected spirals
called a double helix

Alleles

Alleles are	genes in the same location on a pair of chromosomes.
Homozygous means that	the alleles on a pair of chromosomes are the same for a given characteristic.
Heterozygous means that	the alleles on a pair of chromosomes are different for a given characteristic.
A dominant allele	will always express its characteristic.
A recessive allele	will not express its characteristic in the presence of a dominant allele.

45

The word genotype describes	the genes present.
Phenotype describes	the resulting appearance of the organism decided by the genes present and the environment.

Cell reproduction

The two ways by which cells can multiply are	mitosis and meiosis.
Mitosis occurs during	asexual reproduction and growth.
Mitosis results in	daughter cells which are an exact copy of the parent cell.
So, the daughter cells have the same number of	chromosomes as the parent.
The daughter cells are called	clones.

Mitosis

1   A cell nucleus

2   Chromosomes copy

3   ... line up along the centre of the cell

4   ... are pulled apart

5   ... the cell divides.

> **Hint:** Mitosis 'mytoeses'. You have two feet with the same number of toes.

Meiosis occurs during	sexual reproduction.
Meiosis results in	cells that have half the number of chromosomes as the parent cell.
The cells are called	gametes.
After meiosis a human gamete contains	23 chromosomes.

> Meiosis is often called a **reduction division** because it results in gametes (sex cells) with half the number of chromosomes of the parent. The gametes are not genetically identical.

Meiosis

1 — A cell nucleus

2 — Chromosomes copy

3 — ... line up in pairs

4 — ... are pulled apart

5 — ... the cell divides

6 — the pairs of chromosomes are separated in a further cell division.

7

❶uestion

How does sexual reproduction lead to variation?

Human reproduction and sex determination

Sexual reproduction involves the fusion of male and female gametes. The sex of a child is determined by the chromosomes inherited from their parents.

The male gamete is called	a sperm cell.
Sperm is produced in	the testes.
Half the sperm carry a chromosome labelled	X
The other half carry a chromosome labelled	Y
The female gamete is called	an egg cell or ovum.
All egg cells carry a chromosome labelled	X
Egg cells are produced in the	ovaries.
Fertilisation happens when	a sperm and an egg cell fuse together.
Fertilisation usually occurs in	the fallopian tube.
After fertilisation the full number of	chromosomes is restored to the resulting cell.

The fertilised egg is now called	a zygote.
The sex of a child is decided by the	sperm.
Male gender zygotes carry a pair of chromosomes called	XY
Female gender zygotes carry a pair of chromosomes called	XX

Gamete from male

	X	Y
X	XX female	XY male
X	XX female	XY male

Gamete from female

Question

Why is there always the same chance of having a boy or a girl?

Genetic diseases

Some examples of genetic diseases are	haemophilia (sex-linked) cystic fibrosis (recessive gene) sickle cell anaemia (recessive gene) Huntingdon's chorea (dominant gene)

Remember that if the disease appears on a recessive gene, *both* parents must donate the gene for it to show up on the individual. Usually the dominant allele for a characteristic is given a capital letter and the recessive allele for the same charateristic a small letter.

Haemophilia

This disease prevents blood from clotting. A **Punnet square** can be used to show how it is inherited via the X chromosone.

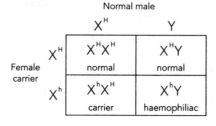

Normal male

	X^H	Y
X^H	$X^H X^H$ normal	$X^H Y$ normal
X^h	$X^h X^H$ carrier	$X^h Y$ haemophiliac

Female carrier

Normal blood (H) clots, wheras abnormal blood (h) does not. The Y chromosone does not carry this gene at all, so the disease is sex-linked via the female

H = normal
h = haemophilia

❷uestions

1   Using a Punnet square (like that used on page 48 for haemophilia), find the probability of a child inheriting cystic fibrosis from two parents who are carriers of the disease. Use F for a normal gamete and f for one carrying cystic fibrosis.

2   The gene for blue eyes is recessive. Look at the family tree below and answer and explain the following:

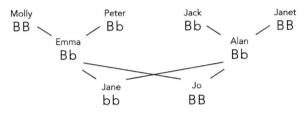

Molly   Peter   Jack   Janet
BB   Bb   Bb   BB
      Emma   Alan
       Bb   Bb

        Jane   Jo
        bb   BB

a   Who is the only member of the family with blue eyes?

b   Could Jo have a child with blue eyes?

Genetic engineering

Sections of DNA can be moved from one species to another to produce useful combinations of characteristics. For example, human insulin can be made by:

1   taking out the required genes from cells, using enzymes

2   putting these genes into bacterial DNA

3   cloning the altered bacteria to produce insulin.

Selective breeding

This involves:

1   selecting parents with desirable characteristics and breeding with them

2   breeding only with the offspring which maintain the characteristics

3   continuing this for generations until the characteristic always shows up.

Some examples of organisms that are selectively bred are	pedigree cats and dogs, meat-yielding farm animals, fruit-yielding plants.
The disadvantage to the organism is	any inherent weaknesses are also reinforced, eg pedigree Dachshunds often have back problems.

Questions

Read the following and answer the questions:

The father of genetics was Mendel. He carried out experiments on sweet peas. He started by growing a pure line of tall plants and a pure line of dwarf plants. He then crossbred them by careful pollination and grew the seeds from each set of plants. Every seed developed into a tall plant. He called these offspring the F_1 generation. However, when he cross-pollinated these F_1 plants, he ended up with a set of plants which were in the ratio of three tall ones to every short plant. These are the F_2 generation.

1   Using T to stand for tallness and t for shortness, write down the pair of alleles for a tall seed and for a short seed.

2   Draw a Punnet square to show the alleles on the F_1 generation.

3   Which is the dominant gene? Explain your answer.

4   Draw another Punnet square to explain the ratio of the F_2 generation.

Cloning

This is the production of identical individuals.

Examples of cloning are:

propagation in plants (including taking cuttings)

micropropagation of plants

splitting early embryos in farm animals, and allowing all the resulting embryos to grow

and more recently with a sheep, removing the DNA from an adult, putting the contents into an emptied egg cell and growing this on to form a clone.

Mutations

These are changes that appear in

gene structure, chromosomes or number of chromosomes.

They are a cause of the variation in life forms because

a mutation might make the organism more successful in its environment.

Mutations of gene structure occur more often when the organism is exposed to

ionising radiation or some chemicals

Down's syndrome occurs in humans when

there is an extra chromosome present in the cells.

The theory of evolution

This is a theory which describes the series of gradual changes over many generations which has led to the huge variety of organisms on Earth.

Natural selection is	the process by which those organisms which are best fitted to survive in their environment succeed.
When the environment changes, failure to adapt results in	extinction.
We know that this has happened on Earth because of	the fossil record.
This shows	changes in existing species and some extinct species.
Fossils are formed by	burial during the formation of sedimentary rocks so that the bones or hard exoskeleton of the organism are preserved. The imprint of the organism may also be preserved.

Two theories of evolution: Darwin proposed that change and variation was driven by the conditions in which the organism lived, so that the most successfully adapted to the environment produced the greatest number of offspring. Changes were brought about by natural mutations. If the change happened to be of benefit, it was carried forward into the next generation. This is called **natural selection**.

Lamarck said that change was driven by the organism. For example, if a giraffe had to continually stretch to reach food, in the next generation the giraffes' necks would be longer, because acquired characteristics could be inherited.

It is generally accepted that Darwin's theory is correct.

Ⓠuestions

Read the following and answer the questions overleaf:

A species of moth, called the peppered moth, is normally light coloured but from time to time a black variety is produced. These moths normally rest on lichen-covered tree trunks and they blend into this background. They are eaten by birds. However, in large towns, the dark-coloured moth often forms over 90% of the population. The atmospheric pollution not only kills many species of lichen but the tree bark and lichen darken with sooty deposits.

1   How have the dark-coloured moths become so successful?

2   Suggest a source of the sooty deposits.

3   What might happen if the large towns became less polluted?

Living things in their environment

Ecosystems

Environmental factors determine to a large degree the types and numbers of plants or animals that live in a given habitat. Biotic factors describe the influence of other living organisms. These include competition, disease and the number of predators. Abiotic factors describe the influence of non-living qualities of the environment. These include weather, water content, soil or air quality. These living and non-living factors make up the **ecosystem**.

A habitat is	the area where an organism lives.
A population is	a group of organisms of the same species.
A species is	a particular set of organisms that can breed with each other and produce fertile offspring.
A community is	all the organisms living in a given habitat.
An environment is	the habitat and its surroundings.
Competition means	a particular plant or animal cannot expand in number indefinitely because they have to share the limited available resources with other organisms.
Plants compete for	light and water.
Animals compete for	food and water and mates.
A predator is	an animal that depends on killing and eating other animals for its food.
The animals they eat are called	prey.
Adaptation means	plants and animals have special features that allow them to live successfully in a given habitat.

For example, polar bears are adapted for cold, snowy weather by:

a thick coat to keep them warm

a thick layer of fat as an energy store and as insulation

a white coat (for camouflage so that they can catch seals) and to reflect the intense rays from the sun

a large body volume with a relatively small body surface to keep heat loss down.

ⓠuestion

Describe how:

a   a camel

·b   a desert cactus

is adapted to the dry desert conditions.

Humans and the environment

Humans take up a lot of the Earth's resources, both in terms of land and materials. We also pollute the planet, and the problem gets worse as the population grows and the application of technology becomes widespread.

Acid rain

The main cause of this is from | burning fossil fuels (eg coal and oil).

The element present in these that is the worst offender is | sulphur.

This burns to | sulphur dioxide.

This dissolves in rain water to give | sulphuric acid.

Another source of acid rain is from | nitrogen oxides.

The high temperature spark in car engines causes | nitrogen and oxygen in the air to combine.

Nitrogen oxide dissolves in rain to give | nitric acid.

Acid rain is bad for | life in rivers and lakes, trees and plant life.

Ozone layer

Ozone is a special form of the element oxygen.

The ozone layer in the upper atmosphere is necessary because	it reduces the harmful ultraviolet radiation from the sun by absorbing it in the upper atmosphere.
The problem is that	there is a marked thinning or 'hole' in parts of the layer.
This is bad for	plankton, which are at the base of food chains in the oceans, and human skin (skin cancer is increasing).
It is caused by	gases including CFCs. These, until recently, were present in refrigerants and aerosols.

CFC stands for chlorofluorocarbons. They act as catalysts in the breakdown of ozone to oxygen.

The greenhouse effect

The greenhouse effect is	the way the Earth stays warm by greenhouse gases trapping the heat from the sun.
Some greenhouse gases are	carbon dioxide and methane.
Global warming is the theory that	the Earth is gradually heating up more and more.
It is thought to be caused mainly by	the increased use of fossil fuels.
This is because	a product of burning fossil fuels is carbon dioxide.
Also cattle produce the gas	methane.
Global warming is a problem because	climate changes are likely to cause many problems.
These include	land being covered with water, new deserts forming, more violent weather, changes in types of crop grown.

Deforestation

Deforestation is caused by	the continual chopping down of trees (the rainforest in South America is a particular problem) to clear land for human use.
It is a problem because	forests lock up carbon during photosynthesis and this reduces the greenhouse effect
	the rainforests contain many unknown plants which could be a rich source of medicines
	the tree roots anchor the soil and absorb much of the water that falls, reducing erosion.

Damaging ecosystems

Man's activities can frequently damage the delicate balance found in ecosystems.

Pesticides are used to	control pests, usually to increase crop yields.
They can cause problems because	their long-term effect on the food chain is not always known.
Fertilisers are used to	return to the soil the nutrients used up by the crops.
They always contain	nitrogen compounds (usually nitrates).
They cause problems because	nitrates are washed into rivers.
This may result in	too rapid growth of water plants
followed by	death and decomposition of some of them
followed by	the decomposing microbes using up the oxygen in the water
followed by	death of all the river life.
This is called	**eutrophication.**

Questions

1   Explain why deforestation may cause:

   a   some animal species to be lost

   b   flooding and soil erosion.

2   Complete the following sentences:

Without the greenhouse effect our planet would not have life as we know it. This

effect keeps the Earth .... , by trapping .... which would

otherwise be lost into .... The trouble is, we now have too much of a

good thing. Burning .... fuels produces the gas ....

.... This is a greenhouse gas like .... , which is produced in the

guts of cows. So, the .... of the Earth is slowly .... One of the

many problems that this could bring is a rise in the sea .... This will be

caused mainly by the fact that water .... when it is heated. There will also

be an increase in the amount of water caused by some melting of the polar

.... caps.

Energy flow in ecosystems

Remember that the source of all energy on Earth is the Sun. The way that energy is passed from life-form to life-form is called a **food chain**.

Producers are	the green plants at the beginning of all food chains.
Consumers are	all the animals in a food chain.
Primary consumers are	the first animals in the chain which feed directly from plants.
Herbivores are	plant eaters (they are primary consumers).
Secondary consumers are	the animals which feed on the primary consumers (they are carnivores).
Carnivores are	animals that eat other animals.

Tertiary consumers are	carnivores that eat other carnivores.
Omnivores are	animals that eat plants and other animals.

Food webs

Food webs show the relationships between more than one food chain. Remember that the arrow always points **from the source** of energy.

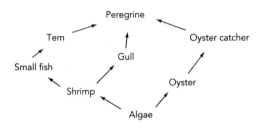

Questions

1   Put the following into a food chain, using as many of the words defined above as possible, so that some have several labels: leaves, foxes, moles, worms.

2   What would happen initially to:

a   the gull population

b   the tern population

if a disease reduced the population of small fish? Explain your answer.

Decomposers

Decomposers are	microbes such as bacteria and fungi which live on the dead material from food chains.
They are important because	they clear up the dead material by breaking it down and they recycle all the nutrients back into the soil.

Pyramids and biomass

Food chains can be described quantitatively, which means that they can be described in numbers. There are two ways of doing this. Either we can give the approximate numbers of each organism in the food chain, or we can give the total approximate mass. Each layer is called a **trophic layer**. The whole energy content is never passed from one layer to the next (only about 10% between trophic layers). The organisms within the layer need energy to maintain themselves, and there is always loss whenever energy is transferred. This means that the size of each layer in terms of mass always gets smaller.

Pyramid of biomass

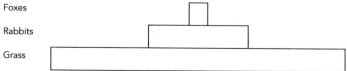

Foxes

Rabbits

Grass

Pyramid of number

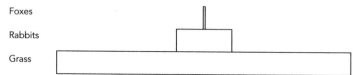

Foxes

Rabbits

Grass

Questions

1   Draw a pyramid in terms of numbers and one in terms of mass for a dog and its fleas.

2   Explain why each trophic layer always decreases in size from the bottom upwards, when we consider the biomass.

The cycles and bacteria

The carbon cycle

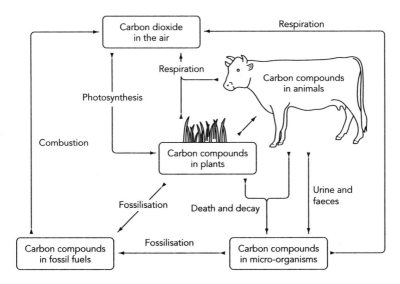

The nitrogen cycle

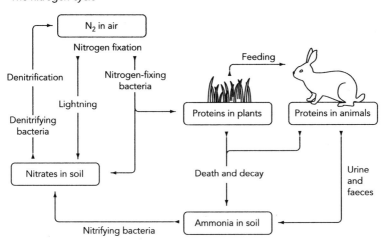

[Don't learn these cycles but understand them enough to answer questions on them or be able to complete a diagram.]

Bacteria in the nitrogen cycle

Decomposing or putrefying bacteria	feed on and break down dead material.
Nitrifying bacteria	turn ammonia in the soil to nitrates.
Denitrifying bacteria	turn nitrates into nitrogen.
Nitrogen-fixing bacteria	turn nitrogen into nitrates.

Food production

With our increasing population, efficient food production is very important. However, tragedies such as BSE (Bovine Spongiform Encephalopathy) can occur. This happened because a cheaper, more efficient method of feeding cows with the remains of dead sheep was introduced. So whatever new steps we take must be done responsibly.

At present, crop yields are increased with	chemical fertilisers.
In future, more use could be made of	planting leguminous plants. Their roots make nitrogen compounds and they are therefore natural fertilisers.
At present, pests are controlled with	pesticides.
In future, pests could be controlled with	a specific natural predator, introduced to the habitat (biological control).
At present, many animals such as poultry and pigs are reared	more intensively and unnaturally.
In future, they could be	reared more naturally. (Their food must still be grown since they are fed on cereals.)
At present, we eat a lot of	meat. In general, an area of land can produce more plant-based food than if the area is used for feeding meat.
In future, we would eat less	meat and more plant-based food.

Materials and their Properties

Classifying materials

Handling materials

The symbols below give the hazards of handling certain materials:

Corrosive

These substances attack and destroy living tissues, including eyes and skin.

Toxic

These substances can cause death. They may have their effects when swallowed or breathed in or absorbed through the skin.

Highly flammable

These substances easily catch fire.

Oxidising

These substances provide oxygen which allows other materials to burn more fiercely.

Harmful

These substances are similar to toxic substances but less dangerous.

Irritant

These substances are not corrosive, but can cause reddening or blotchiness of the skin.

Elements, compounds and mixtures

You should know the following:

Elements are the basic building blocks of chemistry. They cannot be broken down into simpler substances. They are made up of identical atoms, which are represented by a symbol in the Periodic Table of elements. Some elements that you will frequently come across are listed below. Can you identify them from their symbols?

Ca	calcium
Mg	magnesium
Cu	copper
O	oxygen
H	hydrogen
S	sulphur
Cl	chlorine
K	potassium
Na	sodium
N	nitrogen
C	carbon

Compounds are	made from two or more different elements chemically bonded together to make a single new substance. It isn't easy to separate the elements that make the compound.

For example, water is a compound made from hydrogen and oxygen bonded together.

Mixtures are	made from two or more substances which are not chemically bonded together. The substances are usually easy to separate.
Mixtures	have the properties of the substances that they are made from. They can have any composition. Separating a mixture depends on finding a difference in properties between the substances that it is made from.

Separating mixtures

Mixture	Method of separation	Difference in property
Sand and water	Filtration	Sand will not dissolve in water
Salt and water	Evaporation	The water will evaporate away leaving the salt
Dyes in ink	Chromatography (paper)	Dyes run up paper at different rate
Salt and iron filings	Magnet	Salt is not attracted to a magnet
Ethanol and water	Distillation	Ethanol boils at a lower temperature than water
Oil and water	Separating funnel	Oil and water do not mix

Matter

Matter is the name for anything with mass. It is generally thought that all matter is made of tiny particles.

The three states of matter are | solid, liquid, gas.

The properties of each state are different because of | the way the particles are arranged and the way the particles move.

The arrangement of particles in each state is shown here:

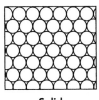 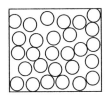 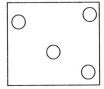

Solid	**Liquid**	**Gas**
close and in a definite pattern	close and random	far apart and random

The movement of particles in each state is shown below:

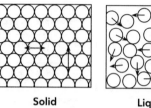

Solid	**Liquid**	**Gas**
vibrating	moving	moving freely

Properties of matter

Shape

Solids have a fixed shape because	the particles are close together and in fixed positions.
Liquids take the shape of their container because	the particles are close together and moving.
Gases have no shape but fill their container because	the particles are far apart and rapidly moving.

Compressibility

Solids cannot be compressed because	the particles are very close together.
Liquids cannot be compressed because	the particles are very close together.
Gases can be compressed because	the particles are far apart.

Change of state

When heated to melting temperature solids turn to liquids because	the particles gain enough energy to break away from their fixed positions.
When heated to boiling temperature liquids turn to gases because	the particles gain enough energy to move far apart.

Expansion

Solids, liquids and gases all expand when heated because	the particles gain energy and therefore can move more rapidly, becoming further apart.

> Remember, the particles do not get bigger – they stay the same size in whatever state the material is in.

Diffusion (This is the spreading out of liquids and gases.)

Solids do not diffuse because	their particles are in fixed positions.
Gases diffuse quickly because	their particles are moving rapidly.
Liquids diffuse slowly because	their particles are very close together and movement is difficult.

Pressure in gases

Gases exert a pressure because the particles are hitting the sides of their containers.

If a gas is heated in a fixed volume the pressure	increases.
This is because	the same number of particles hit the sides of the container with more energy and more often.
If the volume of a given amount of gas is decreased the pressure	increases.
This is because	the same number of particles hit the sides of the container more often when they are squashed into a smaller volume.

Questions

1   Complete the following sentences:

There are .... states of matter: .... , ... and

.... The particles in a solid are regularly arranged, in a ....

position and are vibrating. The particles in a .... are far apart and

moving rapidly. This is why diffusion is so .... Particles in a

.... are close together but free to move, so .... are easy to

pour. They also diffuse but more .... than ....

2   a   What happens at the melting point (melting temperature) as a solid is heated? Explain your answer in terms of particles.

b   What happens to its particles when a substance boils?

3   Explain why the pressure of a gas in a given volume goes down when the gas is cooled.

Atomic structure

Elements are made of	atoms.
The three main sub-atomic particles are	protons, electrons and neutrons.
Atoms of the same element have the same number of	protons and electrons.

The structure of a sodium atom is shown below:

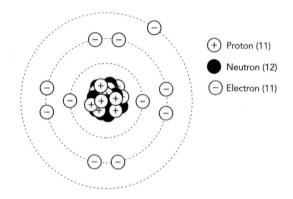

$\oplus$ Proton (11)

● Neutron (12)

$\ominus$ Electron (11)

Relative mass

Electrons	1/1860 (ie approximately zero)
Protons	1
Neutrons	1

Relative charge

Electrons	−1
Protons	+1
Neutrons	0

Mass number and atomic number

In the Periodic Table every element has a symbol with two numbers. For example, lithium is written $^{7}_{3}\text{Li}$ though in some Periodic Tables it may be $^{3}_{7}\text{Li}$.

Either way, the larger of the two numbers is the mass number – in this case 7 – and the smaller – in this case 3 – is the atomic number.

The mass number, A	is the total number of protons + neutrons in the atom.
The atomic number, Z	is the number of protons
This is the same as	the number of electrons.

Remember that atoms are neutral and the positive charge of the protons is neutralised by the negative charge of the electrons, so there must be the same number of each.

You can find the number of neutrons by taking the atomic number (the smaller number) away from the mass number.

For example:

$^{12}_{6}C$

mass number (protons + neutrons)	12
atomic number (protons = electrons)	6
number of neutrons	6

$^{40}_{20}Ca$

mass number (protons + neutrons)	40
atomic number (protons = electrons)	20
number of neutrons	20

$^{4}_{2}He$

mass number (protons + neutrons)	4
atomic number (protons = electrons)	2
number of neutrons	2

$^{23}_{11}Na$

mass number (protons + neutrons)	23
atomic number (protons = electrons)	11
number of neutrons	12

Questions

1 Give the number of protons, neutrons and electrons in the following atoms:

a $^{24}_{12}Mg$ b $^{19}_{9}F$ c $^{39}_{19}K$

2 Fill in the table which describes the sub-atomic particles in an atom:

Atom	A (mass number)	Number of protons	Number of neutrons	Number of electrons
A	16	8		
B		4	5	
C	27			13
D	1			

Isotopes

Many elements have atoms with differing numbers of neutrons. These slightly different forms of the same atom are called **isotopes**.

Only the number of neutrons changes in the different isotopes of an element.

For example:

The atoms below are all the different isotopes of carbon:

$^{12}_{6}C$	Number of protons	6
	Number of electrons	6
	Number of neutrons	6
$^{13}_{6}C$	Number of protons	6
	Number of electrons	6
	Number of neutrons	7
$^{14}_{6}C$	Number of protons	6
	Number of electrons	6
	Number of neutrons	8

The relative atomic mass, A_r

This is the average mass of an atom of an element compared originally with the mass of a hydrogen atom. If there is a significant number of isotopes in an atom, the relative atomic mass will not be a whole number.

Chlorine, for example, is: $^{35\cdot5}_{17}Cl$

and 35·5 is an average of the mass numbers of all the isotopes of chlorine.

For every four atoms of chlorine, three are $^{35}_{17}Cl$ and one is $^{37}_{17}Cl$.

This means that the average mass is: $\dfrac{(3 \times 35) + (1 \times 37)}{4} = 35\cdot5$

At GCSE level, you can usually take the mass number A and the relative atomic mass A_r for most elements as the same.

Questions

Neon has two common isotopes: $^{20}_{10}Ne$ and $^{22}_{10}Ne$.

a   Write down the number of protons, electrons and neutrons in each isotope.

b   Work out the average mass (A_r) of neon assuming there are 90% of the first to 10% of the second. (Hint: This means that in every 100 atoms, 90 will be of one sort and 10 of the other.)

Arrangements of electrons

The electrons orbit in shells (also called energy levels) at a distance from the nucleus. The first shell is nearest to the nucleus. It has the lowest energy. It is always filled first and can hold just two electrons.

Helium

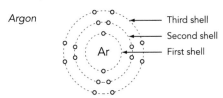

Helium has a full shell

The next shell is further away and can hold up to eight electrons. The third shell holds eight but has reserve space for ten more.

Argon

Third shell
Second shell
First shell

Why does it matter?

The key to understanding the properties of the elements is that chemical reactions depend on the arrangement of the electrons in the atoms and in particular the number of electrons in the outer shell. For example, metals never have more than three electrons in their outer shell, while non-metals always have more than three.

For example, $^{12}_{6}C$ has six electrons in each atom:

Carbon

This may also be written 2,4.

The number of electrons in the outer shell is always the same as the group the element is in. All Group I elements have one electron in the outer shell, all Group II have two electrons and so on. The inert gases in Group 0 are an exception. They all have full outer shells.

If you find that the number of electrons in the outer shell doesn't match the number of the group that the element is in, look for these common errors:

* You have used the mass number instead of the atomic number.

* You have used the wrong number of electrons to fill the shells (four electrons is often used mistakenly for shell two, instead of eight electrons).

* You have forgotten the first shell (which contains two electrons).

Here are more elements – you need only to be able to work out the first 20 elements, up to calcium. Put in the electrons as in the first diagram.

Element	Electron arrangement	Electron diagram
$^{24}_{12}Mg$	2, 8, 2	Mg
$^{16}_{8}O$	2, 6	O
$^{23}_{11}Na$	2, 8, 1	Na
$^{40}_{20}Ca$	2, 8, 8, 2	Ca

Questions

Look at the electron diagram and electron arangements and for each element say:

i   what is the atomic number   ii   which group is it in

iii   is it is metal or a non-metal?

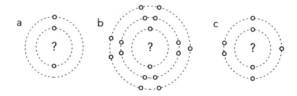

Structure and bonding

Atoms bond together to become stable. The only elements that are so stable that they don't bond and therefore exist as single atoms are the noble gases. They all have full outer shells of electrons. Bonding is all about obtaining full outer shells of electrons.

The three sorts of bonding are	covalent, ionic and metallic.

1 Between non-metals the bonds are

covalent.

The electrons in a covalent bond are

shared.

Fluorine is a gas that exists as pairs of atoms.

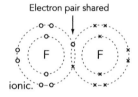

Electron pair shared

2 Between a metal and a non-metal the bonds are

ionic.

Electrons are transferred from the metal atom to

the non-metal atom.

The atoms now have a charge on them.

These charged atoms are called	ions.
Metal ions are always	positive
Non-metal ions are	negative.

For example, when sodium reacts with fluorine the ions are

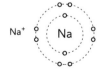

Na^+

3 Metallic bonding exists in

metals

The atoms donate their outer electrons to a common pool or 'sea' of electrons.

Metallic bonding: Metal ions in a pool of electrons

⊕ Metal ion

⊖ Electron

Questions

1 What kind of bonding will the following substances have?

    a water, H_2O b magnesium oxide, MgO

    c carbon dioxide, CO_2 d magnesium, Mg

2 a Oxygen atoms have six electrons in the outer shell. Show how a double covalent bond is formed between two oxygen atoms.

    b The formula for magnesium fluoride is MgF_2. A_rs for Mg = 12 and F = 9. Work out the ions in this compound.

There are two basic structures:

In a **giant structure** the bonding extends throughout the entire substance. Giant structures have high melting temperatures.

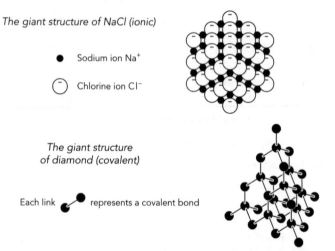

The giant structure of NaCl (ionic)

● Sodium ion Na^+

◯ Chlorine ion Cl^-

The giant structure of diamond (covalent)

Each link represents a covalent bond

In a **molecular structure** the atoms are covalently bonded together in small groups, called **molecules**. Molecular structures have low melting temperatures. In particular, gases, liquids and low melting point solids usually have a molecular structure.

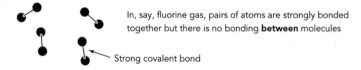

In, say, fluorine gas, pairs of atoms are strongly bonded together but there is no bonding **between** molecules

Strong covalent bond

Type of bonding	Structure
Ionic compounds have	giant structures with high melting temperatures.
Examples	sodium chloride, calcium oxide.
Metals have	giant structures with high melting temperatures.
Examples	copper, iron.
Covalent compounds have	either giant structures with high melting temperatures
Examples	carbon as diamond, silicon dioxide (sand)
	or molecular structures with low melting temperatures
Examples	carbon monoxide, ethanol.

Bonding and conductivity

Bonding affects the way different substances conduct electricity.

Remember that there must be charged particles present that may move to carry the current if a substance is to conduct electricity. Ions (in ionic compounds) are charged particles and metal structures have a pool of electrons – also charged particles.

Covalently bonded substances	never conduct.
Metals	always conduct.
Ionically bonded compounds do conduct	when they are dissolved in water or when they are melted, because the ions are free to move.
Ionically bonded compounds do not conduct	when solid.

Melt or dissolve

Classifying materials

Bonding	Structure	Melting point	Conductivity		
			Solid	Liquid	Aqueous solution
Ionic	Giant	High	Poor	Good	Good
Metallic	Giant	High	Good	Good	N/a
Covalent	Giant	High	Poor	Poor	Poor
Covalent	Molecular	Low	Poor	Poor	Poor

Questions

1 Say what type of structure and bonding each letter represents.

Structure	Melting point	Conductivity	
		Solid	Liquid
W	Low	Poor	Poor
X	High	Poor	Poor
Y	High	Poor	Good
Z	High	Good	Good

2 Which letter could represent each of the following substances and why?

a   platinum

b   carbon in the form of diamond

c   carbon dioxide

d   sodium chloride

3 Complete the following sentences:

Ionic compounds are formed between metal and .... The metal forms

an .... with positive charge and the non-metal forms one with

.... charge. Covalent bonding occurs between ....

.... Ionic compounds have .... structures with ....

melting points. They only conduct electricity when .... or when

dissolved in water. Covalently bonded substances can have either giant or

.... structures. .... structures have low melting temperatures.

Covalently bonded substances do not ....

Ions and formulae

You can use the charges of ions to predict formulae, using the fact that compounds are neutral. The charge of an ion must be cancelled out by the same number of opposite charges on the other ions in the compound.

Some common ions are shown:

Positive ions

+1 Na, K, H, NH_4 (ammonium ion)

+2 Ca, Mg

+3 Al

Negative ions

−1   Cl, Br, I, OH (hydroxide)

−2   O, SO_4 (sulphate), CO_3 (carbonate)

For example, to find the formula of aluminium bromide:

1   Write the ions with their charges Al^{3+} Br^-

2   Make the charge equal Al^{3+} Br^- Br^- Br^-

3   Write the formula $AlBr_3$

Question

Write the formula of:

a   calcium hydroxide

b   sodium sulphate

c   calcium carbonate.

Changing materials

Basic knowledge

What is chemical change? This is the process of making new substances by chemical reaction. The new substances, called the **products**, will have different properties from the starting materials (called the **reactants**).

reactants ⟶ products

Chemical change is usually accompanied by heat changes and is difficult to reverse. Cooking an egg is a chemical change as you can't 'uncook' an egg.

What is physical change? This doesn't produce a new substance. It can usually be reversed. For example, dissolving a substance is a physical change. (You can get the substance back by evaporating the water away.)

Word equations can be used to represent chemical change.

Balanced symbol equations using formulae also represent chemical change.

State symbols may be used to describe the state of the reactants or products:

(s)	means	solid
(l)	means	liquid
(g)	means	gas
(aq)	means	'in aqueous solution' (dissolved in water)

Some formulae to know (with state symbols for practice):

$CO_2(g)$	carbon dioxide gas
$CO(g)$	carbon monoxide gas
$SO_2(g)$	sulphur dioxide gas
$NH_3(g)$	ammonia gas
$O_2(g)$	oxygen gas
$H_2O(l)$	water liquid
$HCl(aq)$	hydrochloric acid solution
$H_2SO_4(aq)$	sulphuric acid solution
$NaOH(s)$	sodium hydroxide solid
$CaCO_3(s)$	calcium carbonate solid
$NaCl(s)$	sodium chloride solid
$CuSO_4(s)$	copper sulphate solid

Add others to this list so that you can test yourself on them.

Tests for gases and for water

carbon dioxide	lime water goes milky
hydrogen	a lighted splint burns with a squeaky pop
oxygen	glowing splint is relit
chlorine	swimming pool smell, bleaches moist indicator paper
ammonia	old urine smell, alkaline gas
water	white (anhydrous) copper sulphate turns blue
	blue cobalt chloride turns pink
	pure water boils at 100°C and freezes at 0°C

Acids and bases

Indicators change colour when added to acids or alkalis in aqueous solution.

Universal indicator is added to a solution to find its pH. It changes colour and the colour is matched to a number.

A neutral solution has a pH of	7
An acidic solution has a pH	less than 7
An alkaline solution has a pH	greater than 7
Acids are neutralised by	bases
A soluble base is called an	alkali

Reactions of acids to form salts

Name of acid	Name of salt formed
hydrochloric	chloride
sulphuric	sulphate
nitric	nitrate

The reactions

reactive metal + acid ⟶	salt + hydrogen
metal oxide + acid ⟶	salt + water
metal hydroxide + acid ⟶	salt + water
metal carbonate + acid ⟶	salt + water + carbon dioxide
ammonium hydroxide + acid ⟶	salt + water

Questions

Complete the following equations:

1   magnesium + sulphuric acid ⟶ .... + hydrogen

2   magnesium oxide + nitric acid ⟶ .... + water

3   sodium hydroxide + ... ⟶ sodium chloride + water

4   .... + hydrochloric acid ⟶ calcium chloride + water + carbon doixide

5   ammonium hydroxide + ... ⟶ ammonium sulphate + water

> **Everyday examples of neutralisation:** Indigestion remedies are often called antacids. They usually contain magnesium hydroxide or calcium carbonate to neutralise any excess hydrochloric acid in the stomach. Acidic soil is neutralised using lime (calcium hydroxide) or limestone (calcium carbonate).

Neutralisation and ions

Acids form hydrogen ions in water, $H^+(aq)$,

eg $HCl(aq) \longrightarrow H^+(aq) + Cl^-(aq)$ (hydrochloric acid)

Alkalis form hydroxide ions in water, $OH^-(aq)$,

eg $NaOH(aq) \longrightarrow Na^+(aq) + OH^-(aq)$ (sodium hydroxide)

Neutralisation between an acid and an alkali produces salt and water:

$HCl(aq) + NaOH(aq) \longrightarrow NaCl(aq) + H_2O(l)$

But $NaCl(aq)$ also exists as ions $Na^+(aq)$ and $Cl^-(aq)$ because the sodium chloride is dissolved in water, so we can write the equation:

$H^+(aq) + \cancel{Cl^-(aq)} + \cancel{Na^+(aq)} + OH^-(aq) \longrightarrow H_2O(l) + \cancel{Na^+(aq)} + \cancel{Cl^-(aq)}$

This becomes a simple ionic equation for the formation of water because all the other ions are the same on both sides of the equation and can be cancelled out:

$H^+(aq) + OH^-(aq) \longrightarrow H_2O(l)$

Useful products from oil

Crude oil, together with natural gas, was formed millions of years ago from sea creatures and organic matter. These were buried by sediments and, under heat and pressure and in the absence of air, they slowly decayed to oil and gases. We drill through layers of impervious rock to find deposits trapped under the surface.

Crude oil and natural gas, like coal, are **non-renewable** resources.

A non-renewable resource is one that	cannot be replaced in a reasonable time.
Crude oil is a mixture of	hydrocarbons.
Hydrocarbons are compounds which contain	hydrogen and carbon only.
The mixture of hydrocarbons that make up crude oil can be separated by	fractional distillation.

Fractional distillation is the process of	heating the oil and collecting the fractions that boil off at different temperatures.
The fractions consist of	a mixture of gas, liquid and solid hydrocarbons with different sized molecules.
The smallest hydrocarbons with 1 to 5 carbons in the molecule are	gases, including methane and natural gas.
The most important liquid fraction contains	petrol.

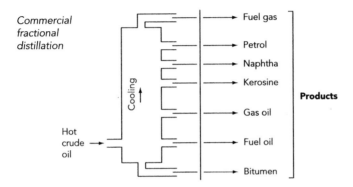

Commercial fractional distillation

Cracking

Large hydrocarbons can be cracked to produce	smaller, more useful, hydrocarbons, particularly petrol.
Cracking is done by	heating the hydrocarbon in the presence of a catalyst.
It is an example of	thermal decomposition.

Don't muddle fractional distillation and cracking. They are both heating processes but fractional distillation is a physical change since it is only a separation of a mixture. Cracking is a chemical change because it produces a new substance.

One important product of cracking is ethene. This is a hydrocarbon with a double bond.

Ethene has the formula	C_2H_4
It can be written in displayed form as	
It is unsaturated because	it has a double bond.

Uses of ethene

Ethene is the starting material for many new materials called polymers.

Polymerisation is a reaction in which | small molecules join together to form large molecules.

For example, ethene is used to make | polyethene.

Ethene ⟶ polyethene (or polythene as it is more commonly called)

polymerisation

Uses of plastics

Polythene is used to make | plastic bags and bottles.

PVC (polyvinyl chloride) is used to make | compact discs.

Polypropene is used to make | crates and ropes.

Problems with plastics

The biggest problem with plastics is that | they don't biodegrade.

This means that | they are not decomposed by living microbes so they stay cluttering the environment for a long time.

Question

Complete the following sentences:

Fractional distillation is the process by which a .... of hydrocarbons which make up crude oil is separated into fractions by .... Cracking is the process by which large .... are heated with a catalyst so that they are broken into short chain molecules. It is done to produce more useful products such as .... Ethene is an important by-product of cracking. It is used to make the polymer .... Fractional distillation is a .... change, whereas cracking is a .... change.

Families of hydrocarbons

Families of hydrocarbons have names.

Alkanes

Alkanes are	saturated hydrocarbons.
Alkanes have	single bonds only.
Alkanes are	unreactive.
The first four alkanes are	methane, CH_4
	ethane, C_2H_6
	propane, C_3H_8
	butane, C_4H_{10}

These can be written as displayed formula where each line represents a covalent bond:

Methane CH_4

$$H - \overset{\displaystyle H}{\underset{\displaystyle H}{\overset{|}{\underset{|}{C}}}} - H$$

Ethane C_2H_6

$$H - \overset{\displaystyle H}{\underset{\displaystyle H}{\overset{|}{\underset{|}{C}}}} - \overset{\displaystyle H}{\underset{\displaystyle H}{\overset{|}{\underset{|}{C}}}} - H$$

Propane C_3H_8

$$H - \overset{\displaystyle H}{\underset{\displaystyle H}{\overset{|}{\underset{|}{C}}}} - \overset{\displaystyle H}{\underset{\displaystyle H}{\overset{|}{\underset{|}{C}}}} - \overset{\displaystyle H}{\underset{\displaystyle H}{\overset{|}{\underset{|}{C}}}} - H$$

Remember '**M**onkeys **E**at **P**eanut **B**utter' to get the first four stem names for hydrocarbons – **m**ethane, **e**thane, **p**ropane, **b**utane.

Alkenes

Alkenes are	unsaturated hydrocarbons.
Alkenes have	a double bond between two carbon atoms.
The first three alkenes are	ethene, C_2H_4
	propene, C_3H_6
	butene, C_4H_8

These can be written as displayed formula where = represents a double covalent bond:

Ethene, C_2H_4

Propene, C_3H_6

Test for a double bond

A double bond can be tested for by adding bromine water.

Bromine water is coloured	brown.
In the presence of a double bond it turns	colourless.
Bromine adds across	the double bond.

For example, with ethene:

Ethene	Bromine	Dibromoethane
(colourless)	(brown)	(colourless)

Fuels

Natural gas is a hydrocarbon, chemical name, methane, formula CH_4. It is an important fuel because it gives out a lot of heat as it burns. Many of the hydrocarbon fractions from the distillation of crude oil are used as fuels.

The products of burning any hydrocarbon are | carbon dioxide, CO_2, and water, H_2O.

hydrocarbon + oxygen ⟶ carbon dioxide + water

If there isn't enough oxygen available, we have **incomplete combustion**. The gas carbon monoxide, CO, is then produced.

Another gas which may be a product of combustion is sulphur dioxide. This is the result of the burning of sulphur impurities in the fuel.

Environmental problems caused by burning fuels

Burning fuels changes the Earth's atmosphere:

The increased release of carbon dioxide into the air	increases the greenhouse effect.
The greenhouse effect is	the warming of the atmosphere by the presence in the air of gases which help the atmosphere to retain heat.

Carbon monoxide is an odourless colourless gas which is poisonous even in small quantities. It is especially dangerous if it is produced in places where the ventilation is poor.

Sulphur dioxide reacts with water and oxygen in the air to produce acid rain. At the high temperature of sparking within a car engine the nitrogen and oxygen in the air react to form nitrogen oxides. These dissolve in water to form acids and are another cause of acid rain.

Too much acid rain	kills fish
	reacts with limestone so wearing away buildings
	damages plant life.
Too much of the greenhouse effect	warms up the oceans
	melts the polar ice-caps
	expands the water in the oceans
	causes flooding
	changes the climate
	creates deserts
	changes the agriculture.

The other main problem is oil spillage at sea.

Oil spillages	have a devastating effect on local wildlife
	are expensive and difficult to clear up
	can have a bad effect on seaside towns which rely on the tourist trade for their living.

Question

Complete the following sentences:

With enough oxygen, hydrocarbons burn to produce .... and

.... If there is not enough .... , the poisonous gas carbon

.... is formed. Atmospheric warming by increased levels of carbon dioxide

is caused by the .... Another atmospheric pollution

problem is .... , caused by acids formed from gases including

nitrogen oxides and ....

Useful products from metal ores and rocks

Typical properties of metals and non-metal elements:

Typical metals	are shiny
	conduct heat and electricity well
	dent but don't shatter when hammered
	have high melting and boiling points
	have high densities.
Alloys are	mixtures of metals chosen to produce a metal with desired properties.

Magnetism is not a typical property of a metal. The only magnetic metals are nickel, cobalt and iron.

Typical non-metal elements	are poor conductors of heat electricity (good insulators)
	are brittle solids (shatter when hammered)
	have low melting and boiling points
	have low densities.

Electrolysis

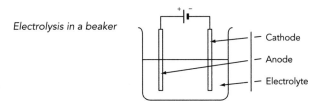

Electrolysis in a beaker

Electrolysis is the process by which, using direct current, electricity is passed through a solution or a liquid containing ions.

The solution or liquid is decomposed by the current at the electrodes.

Gases or metals appear at the electrodes as chemical change takes place.

In electrolysis:

The metal ions are	positively charged.
Metal ions are attracted to	the cathode.
The non-metal ions are	negatively charged.
Non-metal ions are attracted to	the anode.

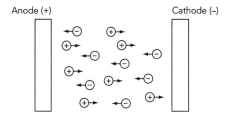

Question

Complete the following sentences:

The anode is the .... charged electrode. The other one is called the

.... The liquid which is electrolysed is called the ....

Metals and reactivity

The metals have an order of reactivity. Below is a list of the more common metals. You will not be expected to learn this list but it helps to have some idea of the metals and to divide them roughly into three groups:

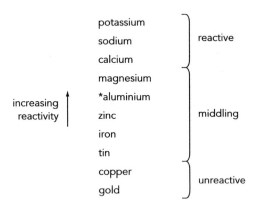

Remember MAZIT for the middling metals.

* Aluminium seems unreactive because it has a permanent layer of aluminium oxide on its surface which protects it from further reactions.

This order holds whatever chemical reaction takes place.

With air	they react less and less readily as we go down the list.
With cold water	only the reactive metals react (though magnesium will very slowly).
With dilute acids	all but the unreactive metals react, though again with decreasing vigour as we go down the list.

Reactions

calcium + oxygen ⟶	calcium oxide
potassium + water ⟶	potassium hydroxide + hydrogen
magnesium + hydrochloric acid ⟶	magnesium chloride + hydrogen
zinc + sulphuric acid ⟶	zinc sulphate + hydrogen

In a chemical reaction, a more reactive metal will displace a less reactive one from a compound.

zinc + copper oxide ⟶ zinc oxide + copper

magnesium + copper sulphate ⟶ magnesium sulphate + copper

These reactions will not go in reverse.

Sacrificial protection: A reactive metal, like magnesium (or zinc), is often attached to a metal such as iron. This is because it is more reactive than the iron and therefore reacts instead of it.

Questions

1 a What is the reactivity list?

   b Why is it useful?

2 Complete the following equations:

   a zinc + oxygen   ⟶ ....

   b sodium + water   ⟶ .... + hydrogen

   c iron + hydrochloric acid   ⟶ .... + hydrogen

   d aluminium + sulphuric acid ⟶ .... + ...

   e magnesium + zinc oxide   ⟶ .... + ...

   f zinc + ...   ⟶ .... sulphate + copper

Minerals and ores

Rocks contain minerals. Minerals are solid elements or compounds (often metal oxides) found in the Earth's crust.

A metal ore contains enough mineral to make it economical to extract the metal.

The way a metal is extracted from its ore depends on	its reactivity.
The reactive metals (above zinc) are extracted by	electrolysis.

Extraction of aluminium

Aluminium is extracted by	electrolysis.
The raw material is	bauxite which contains aluminium oxide.
It is purified and dissolved in	molten cryolite.
This is done because	pure aluminium oxide melts at too high a temperature.

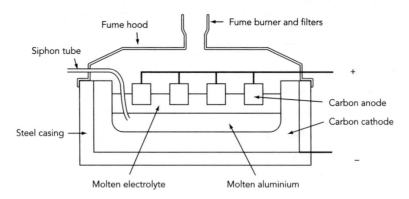

Aluminium ions Al^{3+} are attracted to	the negatively charged cathode and form aluminium.
Oxygen ions O^{2-} are attracted to	the positively charged anode and form oxygen.
This makes the carbon anodes	burn away quite quickly so they have to be regularly replaced.

Half equations for the electrolysis of aluminium oxide

During electrolysis, the same number of electrons is donated at the cathode as is given up to the anode. The equations in brackets show how the same number of electrons is arrived at in this reaction:

At the anode:

The oxide ion loses 2 electrons	$O^{2-} - 2e^- \longrightarrow O \quad (6O^{2-} - 12e^- \longrightarrow 3O_2)$

At the cathode:

The aluminium ion gains 3 electrons	$Al^{3+} + 3e^- \longrightarrow Al \quad (4Al^{3+} + 12e^- \longrightarrow 4Al)$

Uses of aluminium

Uses of aluminium include lightweight vehicle bodies (usually as an alloy), window frames and saucepans.

Oxidation and reduction

Oxidation is the addition of oxygen and reduction the removal of oxygen, but oxidation can also be defined as loss of electrons.

For example, when a metal (M) becomes an ion it is being oxidised.

$$M \longrightarrow M^+ + e^-$$

Reduction is the gain of electrons, so when a metal ion becomes a metal it is being reduced.

$$M^+ + e^- \longrightarrow M$$

As this is the reaction at the cathode, we can say that reduction occurs at the cathode and oxidation at the anode.

Remember: Oil Rig — **O**xidation **I**s **L**oss. **R**eduction **I**s **G**ain.

Iron extraction

Iron, which is below zinc in reactivity, is extracted by using carbon monoxide formed from coke to remove the non-metal (oxygen). This is called reduction of the metal.

iron oxide + carbon monoxide $\longrightarrow$ iron + carbon dioxide

$$Fe_2O_3(s) + 3CO(g) \longrightarrow 2Fe(l) + 3CO_2(g)$$

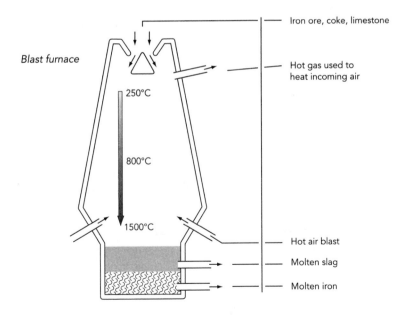

Ⓠuestion

Complete the following sentences:

Iron ore, ... , and .... are fed into the top of the blast furnace. Coke

(carbon) forms carbon .... which is what reduces the iron ore. Limestone

removes the impurities. It is broken down by heat to calcium oxide which reacts with

impurities like sand to form a liquid called ....

Some uses of iron

Uses of iron include steel making and car bodies.

Rusting

Iron is a cheap, strong metal. The biggest problem is that it rusts. This is the name
for the slow corrosion of iron.

In this process iron oxide is formed so rusting is	an oxidation reaction.
For rusting to take place	oxygen and water must be present.
Rusting can be prevented by	painting greasing electroplating.

Purification of metals

Copper is purified using electrolysis:

*Laboratory apparatus
for purifying copper*

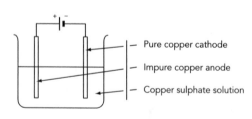

— Pure copper cathode

— Impure copper anode

— Copper sulphate solution

The impure copper is made the anode. During electrolysis, this anode dissolves and
pure copper collects on the cathode.

At the anode	$Cu \longrightarrow Cu^{2+} + 2e^-$
At the cathode	$Cu^{2+} + 2e^- \longrightarrow Cu$

Limestone

Limestone is mainly the chemical | calcium carbonate, $CaCO_3$

It is quarried for use as a building material. It may be crushed and used to neutralise acid soils.

It is heated to produce lime, calcium oxide, CaO.

$CaCO_3$ $\longrightarrow$ | CaO + CO_2

calcium carbonate $\longrightarrow$ | calcium oxide + carbon dioxide

---

This is an example of **thermal decomposition** (heat alone decomposes the calcium carbonate). It is also an example of when knowing a formula helps to work out what happens. This is the removal of carbon dioxide leaving calcium oxide.

Lime reacts with water to produce | slaked lime, calcium hydroxide.

This is used to | neutralise acid soil.

Other uses for limestone are | cement formed by roasting clay and limestone together.

Limestone is also used in the production of: | concrete, formed when cement reacts with sand and gravel.

| glass, where it is reacted with sand and sodium carbonate.

Useful products from air

Air is mostly a mixture of two gases | nitrogen and oxygen.

The percentage of nitrogen is about | 80%

The formula for nitrogen is | N_2

The formula for oxygen is | O_2

Nitrogen is used in the Haber process to make | ammonia.

In this process it reacts with | hydrogen.

The formula for hydrogen is | H_2

The formula for ammonia is | NH_3

The Haber process

The word equation is | nitrogen + hydrogen $\rightleftharpoons$ ammonia

The balanced symbol equation is | N_2 + $3H_2$ $\rightleftharpoons$ NH_3

The raw materials

Nitrogen is obtained from	the air.
Hydrogen is obtained from	natural gas and water.
The catalyst is	iron.
$\rightleftharpoons$ is the sign for	a reversible reaction.

Because it is a reversible reaction, instead of only making ammonia, we end up with a mixture of nitrogen, hydrogen and ammonia. This is because some of the ammonia tends to break down again as it forms. Whenever we deal with a reversible reaction, the conditions of the process have to be adjusted to make sure that as much of the product as possible is converted. In this process a temperature of about 450°C is used and a pressure of about 200 atmospheres.

The Haber process

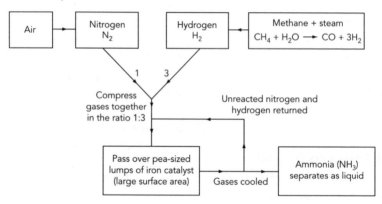

Uses of ammonia

The most important use is to make	fertilisers:
Ammonium nitrate is made by	the reaction of ammonia with nitric acid.
Ammonium sulphate is made by	the reaction of ammonia with sulphuric acid.
Ammonia is also used to make	nitric acid.

Question

Complete the equation for the manufacture of ammonium nitrate:

$$NH_3 + HNO_3 \longrightarrow \quad \dots\dots\dots\dots$$

Nitric acid

Ammonia reacts with oxygen in the presence of a hot platinum catalyst:

ammonia + oxygen	$\longrightarrow$ nitrogen monoxide + water
$4NH_3$ + $5O_2$	$\longrightarrow$ $4NO$ + $6H_2O$

The nitrogen monoxide is cooled and then reacted with water and oxygen:

nitrogen monoxide + water + oxygen	$\longrightarrow$ nitric acid
$4NO$ + $2H_2O$ + $3O_2$	$\longrightarrow$ $4HNO_3$

Problems with fertilisers

We must fertilise our land to obtain better crops, but nitrate-based fertilisers can cause problems. Nitrates dissolve very readily in water and so get carried from the land into the rivers. Here they encourage plant life to grow. This uses up the oxygen in the water, spreads out over the surface and prevents fresh air from dissolving. Gradually the stretch of water dies.

If too large a concentration of nitrates reaches our drinking water there is some evidence that it can be harmful.

Quantitative chemistry

Rules of formulae

1   The symbol for every element has one starting capital letter.

2   A small number after the symbol multiplies the symbol before it.

3   A small number after the bracket multiplies all the symbols inside the bracket.

For example, the formula for ammonium carbonate is $(NH_4)_2CO_3$

The elements in this compound have the symbols	N, H, C, O
The number of N atoms present is	2 (there is 1 inside the bracket and the bracket is multiplied by 2).
The number of H atoms present is	8 (there are 4 in the bracket and the bracket is multiplied by 2).
The number of C atoms present is	1
The number of O atoms present is	3

ⓠuestion

How many atoms of each element are present in:

a Na_2CO_3 ?   b $(NH_4)_3PO_4$?

Relative molecular mass, M_r

We can use relative atomic masses, A_rs, to find the **relative molecular mass**, M_r, of a substance as long as we know its formula.

> The relative molecular mass applies to ionic compounds as well as molecules. It is often called relative formula mass.

For example:

1   Magnesium oxide has the formula MgO

This means that there is | 1 atom of magnesium to every 1 atom of oxygen.

A_r for magnesium, Mg, is 24

A_r for oxygen, O, is 16

M_r for magnesium oxide is

1 x magnesium	1 x oxygen	
1 x 24	+	1 x 16	= 40

2   Carbon dioxide has the formula CO_2

This means there is | 1 carbon atom to every 2 oxygen atoms.

A_r for carbon, C, is 12

A_r for oxygen, O, is 16

M_r for carbon dioxide, CO_2, is

1 x carbon	2 x oxygen	
1 x 12	+	2 x 16	= 44

> The only way to go wrong with these is to misunderstand the way the small numbers and brackets on formulae work. Make sure you understand these points.

ⓠuestion

Find the M_r of:

a   copper oxide CuO

b   sulphuric acid H_2SO_4

c   calcium hydroxide $Ca(OH)_2$

A_rs for H = 1, O=16, S = 32, Ca =40, Cu = 64

Percentage mass

If we know the formula of a compound, we know the ratios of elements present. From these we can find the percentages by mass of the elements present.

You need to work out:

1 M_r

2 the mass of the element present in the compound.

For example, water has the formula H_2O, 2 atoms of hydrogen to 1 atom of oxygen.

A_r for hydrogen, H, is 1 A_r for oxygen, O, is 16

Relative formula mass of water is

$$2 \times \text{hydrogen} \quad 1 \times \text{oxygen}$$
$$2 \times 1 \quad + \quad 1 \times 16 \quad = \quad 18$$

So, the percentage by mass of hydrogen

$$= \frac{\text{mass of hydrogen}}{M_r} \times 100 \qquad = \frac{2}{18} \times 100\% = 11\%$$

The percentage by mass of oxygen is

$$= \frac{\text{mass of oxygen}}{M_r} \times 100 \qquad = \frac{16}{18} \times 100\% = 89\%$$

Question

Given A_rs for H = 1, O=16, Ca =40, Cu = 64

Find the percentage mass of:

a   copper in copper oxide, CuO

b   calcium in calcium hydroxide, $Ca(OH)_2$

Predicting quantities from equations

A balanced equation has the same number of atoms of each element on both sides of the ⟶ sign.

Use the formulae to work out the reacting quantities.

For example, balanced equation $C + O_2 \longrightarrow CO_2$

A_rs/M_rs   12   32   44

The masses should add up to the same number on each side of the equation.

The mole

The relative molecular mass, M_r, and the relative atomic mass, A_r, in grams always contain the same number of particles. We call this a mole.

For example, balanced equation	$C \ + \ O_2 \longrightarrow CO_2$
Masses	12 g 32 g 44 g
	1 mole 1 mole 1 mole

Thus 12 g of carbon, 32 g of oxygen and 44 g of carbon dioxide all contain the same number of particles.

Using moles to find formulae

The number of moles of an element = $\dfrac{\text{Mass of element}}{\text{Relative atomic mass}}$

The number of moles of a compound = $\dfrac{\text{Mass of substance}}{\text{Relative molecular mass}}$

To find a formula

1 Work out the mass of each element present.

2 Work out the number of moles of each element.

3 Work out the ratio of the moles.

4 Work out the simplest ratio of the moles. This gives you the number of atoms of each element and so its formula. (You need to know the symbol for each element.)

For example, 160 g of copper oxide contains 128 g of copper. What is the formula of copper oxide? The A_r for copper is 64 and for oxygen is 16.

1	Work out the mass of each element present	128 g copper		32 g oxygen
2	Work out the number of moles of each element	$\dfrac{128}{64}$		$\dfrac{32}{16}$
3	Work out the ratio of the moles	2	:	2
4	Work out the simplest ratio of the moles	1	:	1

Formula is CuO

Ⓠuestion

32 g of methane, a compound which contains only hydrogen and carbon, contains 8 g of hydrogen. What is the formula for methane?

Sometimes the question comes in terms of percentages. For example, a compound contains 40% calcium, 12% carbon and 48% oxygen. What is its formula?

Turn the % into grams so that it reads 40 g of Ca, 12 g of carbon, and 48 g of oxygen. The answer to this is $CaCO_3$ (calcium carbonate). Check to see if you agree.

Other uses for moles

Moles are used to describe concentrations of solutions. The units are mol/L which stands for moles per litre. For example, a solution of sodium hydroxide, NaOH, with a concentration of 1 mol/L contains 1 mole of sodium hydroxide in a litre of solution. Since M_r for NaOH is 40, this means that the solution contains 40 g of sodium hydroxide per litre.

A mole of **any** gas has a volume of 24 000 cm^3 at room temperature and pressure. For example, how many moles are there in 1200 cm^3 of hydrogen gas, H_2, and what mass of hydrogen is this?

24 000 cm^3 contains 1 mole

1200 cm^3 contains $\dfrac{1 \times 1200}{24\ 000}$ = 0.05 moles

1 mole of hydrogen (H_2) has a mass of 2 g (a mole is the M_r in grams and A_r for H = 1). 0.05 moles has a mass of 2 x 0.05 = 0.1 g

Question

1   How many moles in 60 cm^3 of oxygen gas O_2?

2   What mass of oxygen is this? A_r for O = 16.

The Earth's atmosphere

The main steps in the formation of the atmosphere are as follows (the really major events are in bold):

1   Originally, the **main gas** in the **atmosphere of the Earth** was **carbon dioxide.**

Other gases were **ammonia, methane and water vapour.**

2   The **Earth cooled** and the water vapour turned to water and the **oceans were formed**. Some carbon dioxide dissolved in the oceans.

3   **Plant life developed** and used carbon dioxide for photosynthesis **giving off oxygen**, and **locking up carbon** in their structures.

Bacteria converted ammonia to nitrates.

4   Some of the **oxygen was**

turned into ozone in the upper layers of the atmosphere and acted as a **barrier from harmful radiation** from the Sun.

Oxygen converted

methane to carbon dioxide and water.

5   **Animal life developed** (in the sea and later on land) using

oxygen and giving out carbon dioxide so that the present composition of the atmosphere evolved.

Cycles

Substances such as water, carbon and nitrogen take part in cycles. The carbon and nitrogen cycles are on page 59.

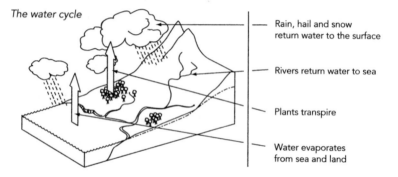

The water cycle

— Rain, hail and snow return water to the surface

— Rivers return water to sea

— Plants transpire

— Water evaporates from sea and land

Question

Complete the following sentences:

Originally, the main gas in the Earth's atmosphere was ....

The oceans were formed when the Earth .... life began in

the .... This released .... into the air, using carbon dioxide for

photosynthesis. Ozone formed in the upper atmosphere, protecting the Earth from

harmful .... life began to develop. This released

.... back into the atmosphere during respiration. Our present

atmosphere has about ....% oxygen and ....% nitrogen.

Geological changes

1	Weathering	rocks are broken up (weathered) in three ways:
	Physical weathering	rain collects in cracks in the rocks, freezes so expanding in size and the rock is forced apart.
	Chemical weathering	rain, which is naturally slightly acidic, reacts with limestone, calcium carbonate.
	Biological weathering	the roots of plants force open cracks.
2	Erosion	exposed surfaces are worn away by processes such as wind and waves.
3	Transport	the movement of rocks (under the force of gravity) by falling or running water.

The Earth's structure

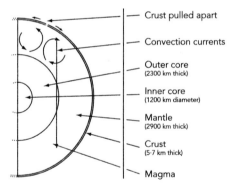

Crust pulled apart

Convection currents

Outer core
(2300 km thick)

Inner core
(1200 km diameter)

Mantle
(2900 km thick)

Crust
(5·7 km thick)

Magma

Types of rock

There are three main types of rock — igneous, sedimentary and metamorphic.

Igneous rock

is formed from cooling molten magma.

An important feature of igneous rocks is crystal size.

The two extremes:

Slow cooling underground produces	intrusive rock with large crystals.
An example of this is	granite.
Fast cooling above ground produces	extrusive rock with small crystals or even a glassy structure.
An example of this is	basalt.

Sedimentary rock

is formed from	weathering of other rocks. The fragments are deposited in deep layers which, under pressure, form rocks.
An important feature of sedimentary rocks is that	fossils are present.
Examples of sedimentary rocks are	mudstone, limestone and sandstone.

Metamorphic rock

is formed from	other rocks by pressure (from deep burial) and high temperature changing the structure of the rock.
Metamorphic rock is often formed	round volcanic action. The hot magma metamorphoses the sedimentary rock through which it erupts.

Metamorphosis changes:

limestone into	marble
sandstone into	quartz
mudstone into	slate.

The rock cycle

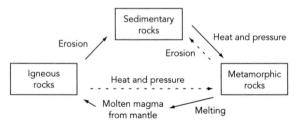

ⓠuestion

Complete the following sentences:

.... rocks are formed from molten .... If this cools slowly, the

rocks will have .... crystals. .... rocks are formed from other

rocks by layers of sediments building up over millions of years. They often contain

.... , which may be used to date them. Metamorphic rocks are formed from

other rocks by heat and ....

The rock record

The rock record provides evidence for geological change.

Rocks can be dated by	the presence of fossils which only lived at a particular time; radioactive dating.
Rocks can be shown to be	tilted, folded and uplifted.

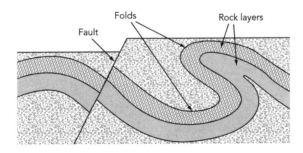

Rocks can be shown to have moved	by matching types of rock or shapes of coastal outlines.

Tectonic plates

The Earth's crust is cracked into a set of	plates.
They move	a few centimetres a year.
They move by	convection currents in the Earth's semi-liquid mantle.
These are caused by heat from	natural radioactive processes in the Earth.

Action of the edges of the plates means:

Rocks are recycled and
mountains formed | when a plate slides under another.

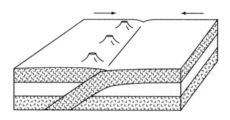

Fold mountains occur | when plates buckle under pressure.

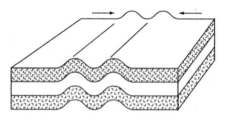

Volcanoes and earthquakes occur | when the plates pull apart or push past
each other.

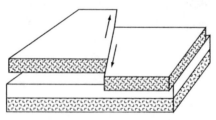

Deep sea spreading | is the gradual spreading of the ocean
floor as plates pull apart and are filled in
with rock erupting from the magma,
during volcanic action.

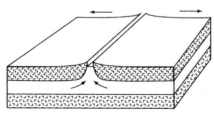

Question

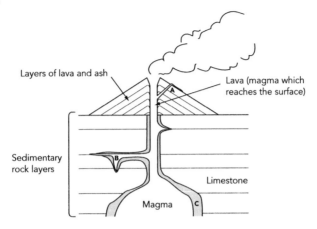

Layers of lava and ash

Lava (magma which reaches the surface)

A

Sedimentary rock layers

B

Limestone

Magma

C

On the diagram A and B will both become types of igneous rock. Describe and explain the difference between them giving a possible example of each type of rock. C is metamorphic. Explain the process by which this rock was formed and suggest the name of a rock that it could have turned into.

Patterns of behaviour

The Periodic Table

In the Periodic Table:

Elements are arranged in order of	atomic number (the number of protons in an atom).
Metals are on the	left.
Non-metals are on the	right.
A period is	a horizontal row of elements.
A group is a	vertical column of elements.
Elements in the same group have	similar properties.
The atoms of elements in the same group have the same number of	electrons in their outer shell.

Question

Fill in the missing labels.

1 **H** Hydrogen 1.0								

Groups
are columns
of elements

Periods
are rows of
elements

I	**II**

3 **Li** Lithium 6.9	4 **Be** Beryllium 9.0

11 **Na** Sodium 23.0	12 **Mg** Magnesium 24.3

1 These are the ....

19 **K** Potassium 39.1	20 **Ca** Calcium 40.1	21 **Sc** Scandium 45.0	22 **Ti** Titanium 47.9	23 **V** Vanadium 50.9	24 **Cr** Chromium 52.0	25 **Mn** Manganese 54.9	26 **Fe** Iron 55.9	27 **Co** Cobalt 58.9
37 **Rb** Rubidium 85.5	38 **Sr** Strontium 87.6	39 **Y** Yttrium 88.9	40 **Zr** Zirconium 91.2	41 **Nb** Niobium 92.9	42 **Mo** Molybdenum 95.9	43 **Tc** Technetium (99)	44 **Ru** Ruthenium 101.1	45 **Rh** Rhodium 102.9
55 **Cs** Caesium 132.9	56 **Ba** Barium 137.3	57-71 Lathanides	72 **Hf** Hafnium 178.5	73 **Ta** Tantalum 181.0	74 **W** Tungsten 183.9	75 **Re** Rhenium 186.2	76 **Os** Osmium 190.2	77 **Ir** Iridium 192.2
87 **Fr** Francium (223)	88 **Ra** Radium (226)	89-103 Actinides	104 **Unq** Unnilquadium (261.1)	105 **Unp** Unnilpentium (262.1)	106 **Unh** Unnilhexium (263.1)	107 **Uns** Unnilseptium (262.1)	108 **Uno** Unniloctium (265.1)	109 **Une** Unnilennium (266.1)

2 This group is called

....

4 This side are

....

3 This side are

....

			III	IV	V	VI	VII	VIII or 0
								2 He Helium 4.0
			5 B Boron 10.8	6 C Carbon 12.0	7 N Nitrogen 14.0	8 O Oxygen 16.0	9 F Fluorine 19.0	10 Ne Neon 20.2
			13 Al Aluminium 27.0	14 Si Silicon 28.1	15 P Phosphorus 31.0	16 S Sulphur 32.1	17 Cl Chlorine 35.5	18 Ar Argon 39.9
28 Ni Nickel 58.7	29 Cu Copper 63.5	30 Zn Zinc 65.4	31 Ga Gallium 69.7	32 Ge Germanium 72.6	33 As Arsenic 74.9	34 Se Selenium 79.0	35 Br Bromine 79.9	36 Kr Krypton 83.8
46 Pd Palladium 106.4	47 Ag Silver 107.9	48 Cd Cadmium 112.4	49 In Indium 114.8	50 Sn Tin 118.7	51 Sb Antimony 121.8	52 Te Tellurium 127.6	53 I Iodine 126.9	54 Xe Xenon 131.3
78 Pt Platinum 195.1	79 Au Gold 197.0	80 Hg Mercury 200.6	81 Tl Thallium 204.4	82 Pb Lead 207.2	83 Bi Bismuth 209.0	84 Po Polonium (210)	85 At Astatine (210)	86 Rn Radon (222)

5 This group is called

....

Key:

6 — Atomic number
C — Symbol
Carbon — Name
12.0 — Relative atomic mass

Groups

Group 0 are called | the noble gases.

They are found in | the air.

Helium is used for | a lifting gas in air balloons.

Neon is used for | red electric discharge lamps.

Atomic structure and chemical reactions:

These gases are unreactive because | they have full outer shells.

They exist as single atoms because | they do not form bonds.

Group 1 are called | the alkali metals.

The first three alkali metals are | lithium, sodium and potassium.

They are all | very reactive, soft metals.

As we go down the group:

the reactivity | increases.

the melting points and boiling points | decrease.

They all react with water to give | metal hydroxide and hydrogen.

The metal hydroxides and metal oxides dissolve in water to give | alkalis.

The word equation is:

metal + water $\longrightarrow$ | metal hydroxide + hydrogen

The metals are stored under oil because | they react with air and with water.

Atomic structure and chemical reactions:

All Group 1 elements have | 1 electron in the outer shell of their atoms.

The alkali metals all form ions with a charge of | +1

The ion is formed by | giving away the outer electron.

As we go down the group, the loss of the outer electron gets | easier.

This means that the reactivity | increases as we go down the group.

Group 7 are called	the halogens (all non-metals).
The names of the first four are	fluorine, chlorine, bromine and iodine.
Appearance:	
Yellow-green gas	chlorine.
Brown liquid	bromine.
Purple solid	iodine.
As we go down the group:	
the reactivity	decreases.
the melting points and boiling points	increase.
Their vapours are	coloured.
They smell like	swimming pools.
They react with water to give	bleaches.
They react with metals to form	salts.

A more reactive halogen will displace a less reactive one from a solution of its salt. (This is exactly the same rule as applies to metals.)

eg chlorine + sodium bromide ⟶ sodium chloride + bromine

Compounds of the halogens:

Salts of the halogens are called	halides.
Hydrochloric acid has the formula	HCl
Sodium chloride (common salt) has the formula	NaCl
Uses:	
Silver halides are used in	photography.
Sodium chloride, dissolved in water, is called	brine.
In industry, brine is electrolysed to produce	hydrogen, chlorine and sodium hydroxide.

Question

Fill in the labels on this diagram:

Laboratory electrolysis of brine

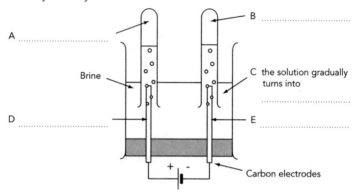

A ....

B ....

Brine

C the solution gradually
turns into

....

D ....

E ....

+   -

Carbon electrodes

Atomic structure and chemical reactions:

The elements exist as molecules with the formula	X_2
All Group 7 elements have	7 electrons in the outer shell of their atoms.
The elements react with metals to form ions with a charge of	−1
The ion is formed by	accepting an electron.
As we go down the group, the gain of the electron gets	harder.
This means that as we go down the group, the reactivity	decreases.

The transition metals

The transition metals are	relatively unreactive metals found in the centre block of the Periodic Table.
Examples of transition metals are	copper, iron and nickel.
Their compounds are often	coloured.
Transition metals and their compounds are often used as	catalysts.
Copper is used	for pipes, electrical wiring.

| Iron is used | for car bodies (in the alloy steel). |
| Nickel is used for | coins. |

Rates of reaction

Chemical reactions happen because the particles of the reacting chemicals bump into each other with enough energy to break bonds. This is called the collision theory. The more collisions there are, and the harder the collision, the faster the reaction.

Example of fast chemical reactions are	an explosion, magnesium burning.
Example of slow chemical reactions are	rusting, rotting.
The factors that change the rate of a reaction are	temperature surface area (of a solid) concentration (of a solution) pressure (of a gas) catalyst.
The definition of a catalyst is that it	speeds up a reaction without itself being used up.

What effects do the factors have?

An increase in temperature makes a reaction go	faster.
An increase in surface area makes a reaction go	faster.
An increase in concentration makes a reaction go	faster.
An increase in pressure of a gas reaction makes it go	faster.
The addition of a catalyst makes a reaction go	faster.

In terms of particles

| An increase in temperature means | the particles are moving faster and with more energy so they collide harder and more often. |
| An increase in surface area of a solid means | there are more available particles to react. |

An increase in concentration of a solution means	the particles collide more often as they are squashed closer together.
An increase in pressure of a gas reaction means	the particles collide more often as they are squashed closer together.
The addition of a catalyst (in some cases)	supplies a surface on which the particles can react.

An example of a typical rate reaction study

Marble chips have the chemical name	calcium carbonate.
They react with hydrochloric acid to form	calcium chloride, water and carbon dioxide.

The apparatus for measuring the rate of reaction is shown below:

Measuring the rate of reaction

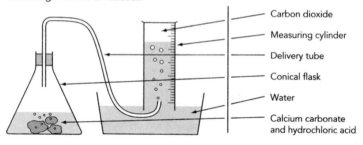

- Carbon dioxide
- Measuring cylinder
- Delivery tube
- Conical flask
- Water
- Calcium carbonate and hydrochloric acid

A typical graph for this kind of reaction would look like the one shown below:

Graph to show reaction rates

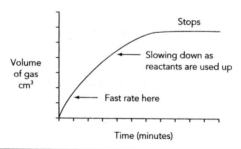

Stops

Slowing down as reactants are used up

Fast rate here

Volume of gas cm^3

Time (minutes)

If you draw a graph, make sure you have the axes correctly labelled and going up in even intervals.

Enzymes

Enzymes are found in living organisms and carry out the chemistry of life at the temperatures of the organism.

Enzymes are	biological catalysts.

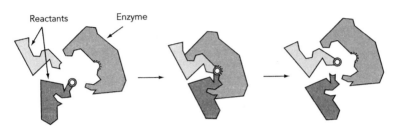

Reactants   Enzyme

Enzymes work by having a particular shape.
A particular enzyme works for a specific reaction.

Uses of enzymes

In wine and beer making, the enzyme comes from	yeast.
In bread manufacture, the enzyme comes from	yeast.
In yoghurt- and cheese-making the enzyme comes from	bacteria.
The process by which enzymes in yeast turn sugar into alcohol and carbon dioxide is called	fermentation.
The word equation is:	
$sugar \xrightarrow{\text{yeast}}$	ethanol + carbon dioxide
If the temperature is too high the enzyme is	denatured (changes shape and so won't work).
Enzymes work best at the right	temperature
	pH (acidity or alkalinity).

Energy transfer in reactions

This topic is about heat changes during chemical reactions. A very important application is to fuels. We rely on the release of energy when fuels are burnt.

If heat is given out to the surroundings in a chemical reaction, the reaction is called	**exothermic**.
The temperature of the reaction	rises.
If heat is taken in from the surroundings during a chemical reaction, the reaction is called	**endothermic**.
The temperature of the reaction	falls.

Energy level diagrams represent these reactions, for example:

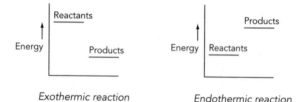

Exothermic reaction   Endothermic reaction

Bond breaking

All chemical reactions happen because bonds between atoms are broken and new ones formed.

When bonds are broken, energy is	taken in.
When bonds are formed, energy is	given out.
If more energy is taken in than given out, the reaction overall is	endothermic.
If more energy is given out than taken in, the reaction overall is	exothermic.

Activation energy

Activation energy is the initial energy required to break bonds. A catalyst lowers the activation energy for a reaction as shown:

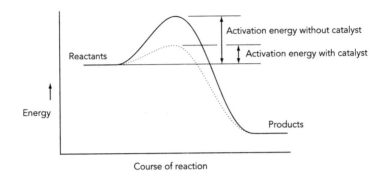

Course of reaction

Bond energies

These involve simple sums so always try to do them in an exam. The key to remember is that each bond has a given energy value which is the same whether the bond is broken or formed. For example, C – H bond energy 413 kilojoules/mol. This is put in to break the bond and given out when the bond is formed.

Bond	Energy kJ/mol
O = O	498
C – H	413
C = O	805
O – H	464
C = C	612

When methane burns to give carbon dioxide and water, for example, the reaction can be represented in displayed formula, which shows all atoms and all bonds:

$$\begin{array}{c} H \\ | \\ H-C-H \\ | \\ H \end{array} + 2\ O{=}O \longrightarrow O{=}C{=}O + 2\ O\begin{array}{c} H \\ \diagup \\ \diagdown \\ H \end{array}$$

On the left-hand side bonds are broken, so heat is	taken in.
Number of C – H bonds	4
Number of O = O bonds	2
So total energy needed to break these bonds is	(4 x 413) + (2 x 498) = 2648 kJ/mol
The energy is put in so the sign is	positive.
On the right-hand side bonds are formed, so heat is	given out.
Number of C = O bonds	2
Number of O – H bonds	4
So total energy given out when these bonds form is	(2 x 805) + (4 x 464) = 3466 kJ/mol
This energy is given out so the sign is	negative.
The heat of reaction, ΔH, which is the difference, is	–818 kJ/mol
So the reaction is	exothermic.

The heat of reaction ΔH is **negative** if the reaction is **exothermic** and **positive** if the reaction is **endothermic**.

Question

Using bond energies, find ΔH and say whether the reaction is exothermic or endothermic.

Reversible reactions

Some reactions are reversible.

$$\text{Reactants} \rightleftharpoons \text{Products}$$

The sign $\rightleftharpoons$ means that the reaction is reversible. In fact, reaction never stops but is continuing in both directions at the same time. The forward rate is exactly the same as the backward rate, so the reaction has reached equilibrium and we can see no change in the composition of the mixture of reactants and products. This is called a **dynamic equilibrium**.

The Haber process for making ammonia is reversible:

$$N_{2(g)} + 3H_{2(g)} \rightleftharpoons NH_{3(g)} \qquad \Delta H = -92 \text{ kJ/mol}$$

This is an exothermic reaction from left to right.

To get the best yield use	low temperature and high pressure.
A compromise temperature is used because	low temperature would be too slow.
A compromise pressure is used because	high pressure would be too expensive.

Le Chatelier's Principle: This is an aid to predicting how changing conditions, such as temperature or pressure, will affect a reaction. It says that if you impose change on a system at equilibrium, the equilibrium will change to minimise the disturbance. This sounds very hard, but it is a useful aid and easy to use.

For example, all the chemicals in the Haber process are gases. What happens if we increase the pressure? The equilibrium must change to produce less pressure. There are fewer gas particles on the right, which means less pressure, so the equilibrium will move to the right.

Physical Processes

Electricity and magnetism

Electrical circuits

> **Hint:** An electric current through a wire is a flow of electrons, which are tiny negatively charged particles. It can help to picture these as rain drops, so that you compare current to a flow of water.

The symbols for components in a circuit are as follows:

—⊣⊢—	Cell
—⊣⋯⊢—	A battery (more than one cell connected together)
—o∿o—	a.c. power supply
—⊗— or —◯—	Filament lamp
—o⁀o—	Switch
—▭—	Fuse
—▭—	Fixed resistor
—▱—	Variable resistor
—Ⓜ—	Motor
—▭▭—	Heater
—Ⓐ—	Ammeter
—Ⓥ—	Voltmeter
—◁⏐—	Light-emitting diode (LED)
—▱—	Thermistor
—▭—	Light-dependent resistor (LDR)

Components in a circuit may be arranged in parallel or in series.

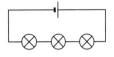

Three bulbs
connected in series

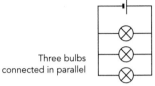

Three bulbs
connected in parallel

The main differences between series and parallel circuits are given below. The really important differences that you must know are the ones in bold. The others follow from this anyway.

In a series circuit

The same current flows through	**each component.**
The potential difference (voltage) across each component depends on its	resistance.
The total resistance is equal to	the sum of the separate resistances.
The total potential difference is equal to	the sum of the separate potential differences.

In a parallel circuit

The voltage across every component of a circuit is equal to	**the voltage across the cell (battery).**
The current through each component of a circuit depends on	its resistance.
The total current is equal to	the sum of the currents through the separate components.

Measuring current

The units which are used for measuring current are	amperes (or amps).
These have the symbol	A.
The instrument for measuring current is the	ammeter.
It is always placed in the circuit	in series with the component.
In a series circuit, the current is	the same all the way round.

In a parallel circuit, the total current that enters any junction is	equal to the total current coming out of the junction.
The symbol for current is	I.

Questions

1 Complete the following sentences:

A current will flow through a component in a circuit if there is a ....

(potential difference) across its ends. The larger the voltage the .... the

current. Components in a circuit resist current. The greater the resistance, the

.... the current.

2 a Draw a circuit which includes one battery and two bulbs:

    i   in parallel   ii   in series.

  b Add an ammeter to each diagram which will measure the current flowing through one of the bulbs.

3 Write down the readings which are missing in the ammeters in the circuits:

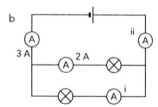

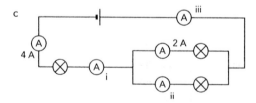

A circuit is usually composed of two sorts of components (plus wires):

One which **supplies** energy such as	battery, solar cell, mains power supply.
Components that **use** energy including	lamps, buzzers, resistors, motors.

When current flows through a resistor, the resistor	heats up.
If we increase the resistance in a circuit, the current	decreases.

The variable resistor

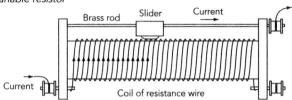

Question

Complete the following sentences:

The variable resistor or rheostat is made from a long piece of .... , made

into a coil. The .... of wire included in the circuit is varied by moving the

slider. The .... the piece of wire, the greater the resistance. When a resistor

is included in a series circuit containing a bulb, as the length of wire included in the

circuit increases, so the brightness of the bulb ....

Measuring voltage

The units used for measuring voltage are	volts.
These have the symbol	V.
The instrument used for measuring voltage is a	voltmeter.
It is always inserted in a circuit in	parallel with the component whose voltage is being measured.
The symbol for voltage is	V.

Measuring battery voltage

Question

1 What is the missing reading on the voltmeters in the following circuits?

  a   b   c

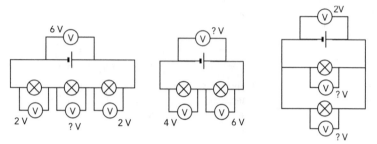

2 Redraw the circuit below to include an ammeter and a voltmeter to measure the current through, and the voltage across, the lamp.

A muddling detail: The electromotive force or e.m.f. of a **battery**, is also measured in volts. This produces a potential difference or p.d. across the **components** of a circuit, also measured in volts. Voltage is a rather loose term which describes both.

Resistance

The units used to measure resistance are	ohms.
These have the symbol	Ω.
Resistance is found by measuring	voltage and current.
The capital letter used to denote resistance is	R.

Factors which affect the resistance of a wire

Metals vary in their ability to resist the flow of current. Copper, for example, has a lower resistance than nickel (for the same size and shaped piece).

The longer the wire	the greater the resistance.
The thicker the wire	the smaller the resistance.

Resistance also depends on	temperature.
The hotter the wire	the greater the resistance.

Ohm's Law

Remember this applies to metals at constant temperature.

Ohm's Law states that	Resistance = p.d. ÷ current
In symbols this is	R = V/I

> **Hint:** This is more easily remembered as V = R x I (the **V**icar teaches **R**eligious **I**nstruction), but you will have to rearrange it to find the resistance.

Ⓠuestions

1 Rearrange Ohm's Law to find I.

2 Work out the resistance of the bulb in each of the following circuits:

a

b

How current may vary with voltage

If we draw a graph of voltage against current, the slope of the graph gives us the resistance. If the material obeys Ohm's Law we have a straight-line graph. Learn the shapes of the graphs.

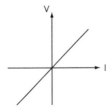

Resistor at constant temperature

The resistance stays constant

The current through a resistor (at constant temperature) is	directly proportional to the voltage.
This means that as one goes up	the other goes up at the same rate.

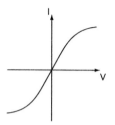

A filament

The resistance gets greater
as the current increases
(and it gets hotter)

As the voltage increases, the current increases but	more and more slowly.
This is because as the filament gets hotter	its resistance increases
and so the current	decreases.

A diode

No current flows when
the voltage is reversed

The current through a diode only flows	in one direction.
The resistance in the other direction is	very high.

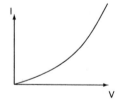

Thermistor

The resistance gets less
as the current increases
(and it gets hotter)

The symbol for the thermistor is	
As the voltage increases the current increases but	more and more rapidly.
This is because as a thermistor gets hotter its resistance	decreases (and the current increases).

Light-dependent resistor (LDR)

The symbol for the LDR is	
The resistance of an LDR depends on	the brightness of light shining on it.
As the brightness increases the resistance	decreases.
This means that in bright light it will conduct electricity	more easily.

Units

Charge

Charge is measured in	coulombs.
Charge has the symbol	Q.
An amp is	1 coulomb per second.
So, coulombs	= amps x seconds
The equation for charge is	$Q = I \times t$

Energy

The units for energy are	joules.
The units for volts are	joules per coulomb.

> **Hint:** The source of energy (measured in joules) in a circuit is the battery or power pack, so volts and joules must be related. If you also remember that the greater the voltage of the supply, the more energy is given to each coulomb (charge) to carry round the circuit, then volts measure the energy per unit of charge so volts = joules per coulomb.

Power

Power is	the rate of using (transferring) energy.
The units for electrical power are	watts.
These have the symbol	W.
The equation to remember is	Power, P = V x I (watts = volts x amps)
1000 watts is called	1 kilowatt.
This has the symbol	kW.
Watts can also be expressed as	joules per second.

Fuses

The symbol for a fuse is	
Fuses are marked with the amount of	current they can carry.
If too much current passes through a fuse wire, it	melts.

Ⓠuestion

Use the equation watts = volts x amps to find a suitable fuse for each of the appliances shown below, from fuses rated 3 A, 5 A, or 13 A assuming a voltage of 230 V. Remember that the fuse must be larger than the required amount of current but by the smallest margin possible.

a

1000 W hairdryer

b

1.5 kW kettle

Mains electricity

Batteries and cells produce direct current usually shortened to	d.c.
The direction of this current through the circuit is	always the same.
Mains electricity supplies alternating current, symbol	a.c.

The direction of this current	alternates many times per second.
Mains electricity supplies a voltage of about	230 V.
It has a frequency of	50 cycles per second.
'Cycles per seconds' are called	hertz.
These have the symbol	Hz.

Wiring a plug

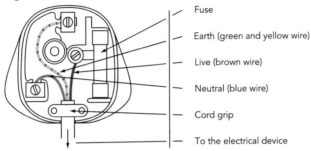

Fuse

Earth (green and yellow wire)

Live (brown wire)

Neutral (blue wire)

Cord grip

To the electrical device

The brown wire is connected to	the live terminal.
The blue wire is connected to	the neutral terminal.
The green and yellow wire is connected to	the earth.
Electricity is supplied to a house through	the live wire.
The fuse is placed in the	live wire.
The neutral wire provides	the return path for the current.
In normal use no current passes in	the earth wire.
The symbol for the earth terminal is	$\perp$
The plug case is made from plastic (or rubber) because	plastic and rubber are good insulators of electricity.
The wires are made from copper because	copper is a good conductor of electricity.
A good insulator is the same thing as	a poor conductor.

Protecting the users of electrical appliances

Some protection is given by	circuit breakers and fuses
	the earth wire, double insulation of appliances
	earthing appliances which have metal covers.

Residual current circuit breaker

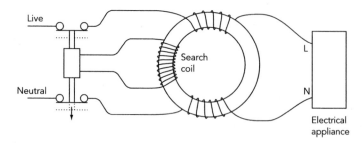

ⓠuestion

Complete the following sentences:

In a residual current circuit breaker, the live and neutral wires are wound in

.... directions around an iron ring. Normally the magnetic effects caused by

the two currents cancel because they are the .... If a fault causes more

current to flow in one of the wires, the ring becomes .... Now a current

flows in the .... coil. This trips a switch which cuts off the ....

Fuses are designed to .... when they are overheated. This is why it is very

important that the fuse with the correct .... is fitted to the appliance.

The earth wire

One possible fault in an electrical appliance involves a live wire touching the metal case of the appliance.

If a person touches the faulty appliance	the electricity could flow to earth through the person's body.
An earth wire connects	the metal case to the earth (via the plug).

If the appliance is case then becomes live	the electricity flows to earth through the earth wire.
This is because the earth wire	provides a return path to earth with less resistance than the human body.
The larger than normal current produced in the live wire causes	the fuse to melt.

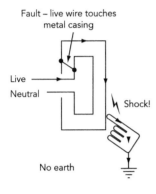

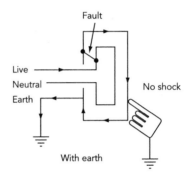

Double insulation

If the casing of an appliance does not conduct electricity it does not need	an earth wire.
The casing of the appliance provides	protection.
Hairdryers have no earth wire because	they are doubly insulated.

Electrical heating

An electric current heats up any parts of a circuit which have	resistance.
This heating effect is used in the home for	cookers, room heaters, water heaters.

Try to add five more examples of your choice.

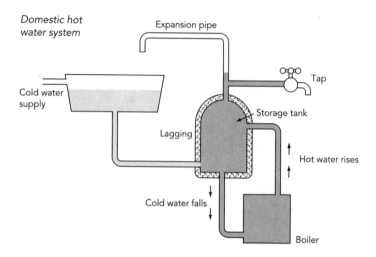

Domestic hot water system

Expansion pipe

Tap

Cold water supply

Storage tank

Lagging

Hot water rises

Cold water falls

Boiler

Questions

1   Where does the cold water enter the tank?

2   Why is the tank lagged?

3   Where in the storage tank is the water hottest?

4   Explain your answer to 3.

Calculating the cost of using electrical appliances

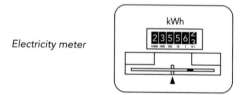

kWh

Electricity meter

The unit used for working out the energy used is	the kilowatt-hour.
The equation to learn is	Energy consumed = power x time.
The units are	kW h, ie kW x hours.
One kilowatt is equal to	1000 watts.

> **Hint:** Energy is measured in joules but in domestic electricity it is measured in kilowatt-hours. In fact, we could use joules but it makes the numbers smaller if we use kilowatt hours.

Energy transferred	= power x time
Joules	= watts x seconds
and 1 kW h is the same as	1000 watts x 3600 seconds
1 kilowatt-hour	= 3 600 000 joules

Questions

1 A 1000 W electric fire is used for 5 hours. What is the cost at 7p per kW h?

2 A 0.6 kW vacuum cleaner is used for 2 minutes. What is the cost at 8p per kW h?

Electric charge

Static electricity

When two surfaces rub together it is possible that each will become charged.

There are two sorts of charge	positive and negative.
Like charges	repel each other.
Unlike charges	attract.
Charge is caused by the transfer of	electrons.
These have a charge which is	negative.
The surface which gains electrons will have a charge that is	negative.
The surface that loses electrons will have a charge that is	positive.
The size of the charge on each surface will be	equal.
The greater the distance between the oppositely charged surfaces	the smaller the attraction.

Surfaces

Metals are good	conductors.
Non-metals conduct	poorly.
Poor conductors are called	insulators.

129

Charge can build up on materials that are	insulators.
An example of an insulator is	plastic.
A charged conductor can be discharged by	connecting it to the earth with a conductor.

ⓠuestion

Draw the charges on the cap and the leaves of each electroscope:

a

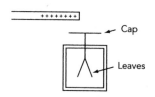

b

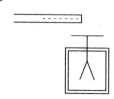

Uses of static electricity include:

Cleaning up the air because	electrostatic charge attracts very light particles. If the chimneys of power plants are charged, they trap the smoke and stop it from polluting the air.
Electrostatic photocopiers because	carbon is attracted to the charged places on the paper and then heat sealed to give a copy.
Spray painting of surfaces because	if the surface is negatively charged it will attract fine droplets of positively charged paint in an even coat.

Some problems caused by static electricity

1 Filling an aeroplane with fuel from a tanker because	if any charge has built up on the aeroplane it may be discharged to earth. The spark could cause a fire in the fuel.
2 Anywhere where there are finely divided particles (like sawdust) because	if there is a build up of charge for any reason it could be discharged to earth with a spark.
The spark can cause a fire because	the small particles have a huge surface area exposed to the oxygen in air.

ⓠuestion

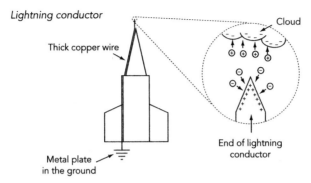

Lightning conductor

Thick copper wire

Cloud

End of lightning conductor

Metal plate in the ground

Complete the following sentences:

When hail and ice particles .... against each other in a storm cloud, under

the right conditions a large .... can build up in the cloud. A flash of

.... occurs when static charge leaves the bottom of the thundercloud. A

lightning flash can release hundreds of millions of .... of energy and this can

cause a lot of damage. Many .... buildings have a lightning conductor. This

is made of .... One end is buried in the .... near the building.

The other end is .... As the charged cloud nears the point, a charge of

.... sign is induced at the point. The air between the cloud and the point

forms ions and some of the charge on the cloud is neutralised by these.

Electrolysis

When some chemical compounds are dissolved in water or melted, the resulting liquid conducts electricity and is called an **electrolyte**.

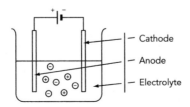

Cathode

Anode

Electrolyte

A chemical compound contains	more than one element.
An electrolyte contains	ions.
During electrolysis, ions move to the	electrodes.
Negative ions are attracted to the	positive electrode.
This is called the	anode.
Positive ions are attracted to the	negative electrode.
This is called the	cathode.
The electrolyte is split into	elements.
The process is called	electrolysis.

Question

Complete the following sentences:

The amount of substance released at the electrodes .... as the current increases.

The longer the current flows, the .... the amount of substance deposited.

Reminder about units

Charge is measured in	coulombs.
Charge (coulombs) =	current (amps) x time (seconds)
The equation is	$Q = I \times t$

Questions

1   How much charge is moved when:

   a   A current of 4 amps is passed through an electrolyte for 30 seconds?

   b   A current of 6 amps is passed for 2 minutes?

   c   A current of 5 amps is passed for 1 hour?

2   In which of the above would the greatest amount of substance be deposited at the electrodes?

Electromagnetic forces

Bar magnets

The ends of a bar magnet are called	poles.
The two poles seek	north and south.
If a bar magnet is suspended, the north-seeking pole will point towards the	north.
Unlike poles	attract.
Like poles	repel.
The magnetic field around a magnet exerts a force on	magnetic materials.

Ⓠuestion

Complete the field lines round the bar magnet and put in arrows to indicate the direction that a north-seeking pole would point.

Electromagnetism

When a current passes through a wire, a magnetic field is produced around the wire.

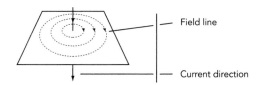

Field line

Current direction

Solenoid

When a current passes through a coil of wire (or **solenoid**) the field is shaped like that of a bar magnet.

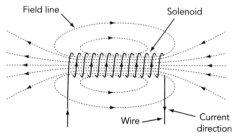

The strength of the field increases when:

the current through the coil is increased

the number of turns in a given length of coil is increased

there is an iron core inside the coil.

Ⓠuestion

Complete the following sentences:

The arrows that show the direction of the magnetic field point from the ....

pole to the .... pole. To remember the direction of the magnetic field round

a wire carrying a current, we use the .... rule. If we imagine a wire entering

the page at right angles, with the current flowing into the page, then the magnetic

field around the wire is in a .... direction.

Uses of electromagnets

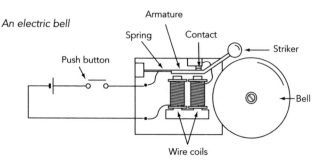

An electric bell

Question

Complete the following sentences:

How an electric bell works

When the circuit is completed, a .... flows. This turns the coils of wire into

an .... The electromagnet attracts the soft iron .... and this

movement causes the .... to hit the bell. When the bell is struck, the

contact is broken and the coil is no longer a .... A spring pulls the soft

iron back and the circuit is complete again.

The motor effect

When a current-carrying wire is placed in a magnetic field, there is a force on the
wire that may make it move.

The magnetic field has produced a force on	the current-carrying wire.
The force is greatest if the magnetic field is at	right angles to the wire.
The direction of the force is always at right angles to	the magnetic field and the wire.

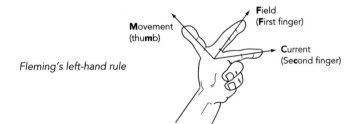

Fleming's left-hand rule

Movement (thumb)

Field (First finger)

Current (Second finger)

The direction of movement is given by	Fleming's left-hand rule.
The thumb and first and second fingers of the left hand are held at	right angles to each other.
The first finger represents the direction of	the magnetic field.
The second finger represents the direction of the	current.
The thumb represents the direction of	movement of the wire.
If the current is reversed, the wire	moves in the opposite direction.
If the direction of the magnetic field is reversed, the wire	moves in the opposite direction.

> **Hint: Motors** drive on the **left**-hand side of the road. Fleming's left-hand rule tells us the direction of the **motor** effect.

The electric motor

The basis of the electric motor is the interaction between a magnet and the magnetic field from an electromagnet to produce a turning motion.

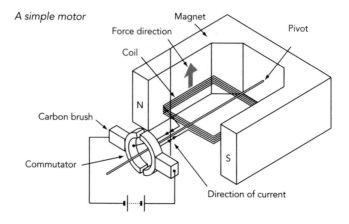

A simple motor

Magnet · Pivot · Force direction · Coil · Carbon brush · N · Commutator · S · Direction of current

Question

1 Complete the following sentences:

When current flows through the coil, a .... is produced

round the coil. This cuts the field from the fixed .... and a force is

produced at right angles to both the magnetic field and the .... There

is an upward force on the left-hand side of the coil and a .... force on

the other side. These forces .... the coil. The .... allows the

coil to turn continuously. As it does this, it ensures that the current always flows in

the .... direction round the coil. (In this case it flows towards the

commutator in whichever arm of the coil is on the left.)

2 The brushes on a commutator are usually made of carbon (graphite). Why is this a good material to use?

Electromagnetic induction

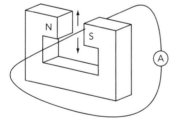 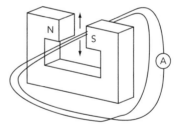

This is how electrical potential differences are produced in a wire moving through a magnetic field. This p.d. can produce a current. We get the same result from moving a magnet past the wire or coil.

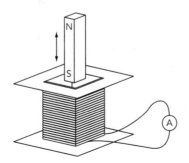

A larger deflection can
be produced by

having more turns of wire on the coil

using a more powerful magnet

moving the magnet in and out of the coil
more quickly

having a larger coil area.

Generating electricity

A generator produces electricity:

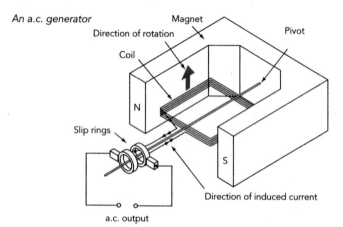

An a.c. generator

The direction of the current in the external circuit reverses each time the coil turns.
This type of current is called alternating current (a.c.).

Transformers

Transformers change voltage. They use coils of wire wound around an iron core, with
different numbers of turns.

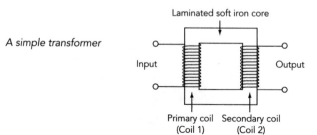

A simple transformer

If the output voltage is less than the input voltage we have	a **step-down** transformer.
If the output voltage is more than the input voltage we have	a **step-up** transformer.
The current must be	alternating (a.c.).

The equation to know is:

Number of turns on coil 2		Voltage across coil 2
────────────────────────	=	────────────────────
Number of turns on coil 1		Voltage across coil 1

In symbols	$\dfrac{N_2}{N_1} = \dfrac{V_2}{V_1}$
The laminated iron core helps reduce	eddy currents.
These would heat up the iron core and energy would be	wasted.

Hint: Coil 1 is often called the primary coil and coil 2 the secondary coil. Notice that this equation can be turned upside down and is still true: $\dfrac{N_p}{N_s} = \dfrac{V_p}{V_s}$

Also, the equation can be rearranged to $N_s V_p = N_p V_s$

Questions

1 The input on the primary coil of a transformer is 240 V a.c.. The primary coil has 1000 turns. If the output is 12 V a.c., how many turns are there on the secondary coil?

2 Find the voltage if the input voltage is 240 V a.c. when the number of turns are as shown:

	Primary (coil 1)	**Secondary (coil 2)**
a	100	200
b	150	50
c	1920	40

3 Complete the following sentences:

A step-down transformer has a .... output voltage than ....

voltage. The secondary coil has .... turns than the .... coil.

Transformers only work if the current is ....

> **Hint:** Transformers don't produce something for nothing. The energy going into the transformer every second, the input power, must be the same as the energy coming out every second, the output power, (ignoring any losses). But power = V x I. So, volts$_1$ x amps$_1$ = volts$_2$ x amps$_2$. So if the voltage is stepped **up**, the current is stepped **down** by the same factor.

Mains electricity is generated by rotating an electromagnet within coils of wire. The turning motion is provided by turbines which are turned by a variety of energy sources. Most power stations use steam formed from water using either fossil fuels or nuclear energy as the source of heat.

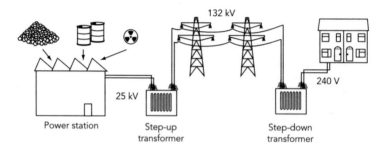

Alternative energy sources include	solar, wave, wind, flowing water.
The current generated is	alternating (a.c.).
This is because the voltage must be stepped up using a	transformer.
Mains electricity is transmitted at a high	voltage.
This is so that it is transmitted with a low	current.
The smaller the current in the transmission wires	the smaller the heat loss
	the thinner the cables can be.

Ⓠuestion

Why is mains electricity:

a   transmitted at high voltage

b   transmitted as a.c.?

Forces and motion

Mass and weight

The unit of mass is the	kilogram (kg).
The unit of force is the	newton.
The symbol for the newton is	N.
Weight is measured in	newtons.
This is because weight is a	downward force.
On the Earth, gravity pulls down with a force of	10 newtons per kilogram (more accurately 9.8 N/kg).
These units are shortened to	N/kg.
To find the weight of a particular mass (on Earth)	multiply the mass in kilograms by 10 (more accurately 9.8).

Speed and velocity

The equation to find speed is	$\text{Speed} = \dfrac{\text{Distance travelled}}{\text{Time taken}}$
Velocity is	speed in a given direction.

Questions

1 What is the weight on Earth of:

   a a 10 kg mass   b a 10 g mass

   c a 0.1 kg mass?

2 Find the speeds of the following cars, using the correct units in your answers:

	Distance	**Time taken**
a	200 miles	2 hours
b	200 kilometres	4 hours
c	10 metres	5 seconds
d	200 cm	0.5 seconds

Hint: We often use speed and velocity to mean the same thing in everyday life. If we use the term 'velocity' we must specify the direction. So, 20 km/h is a car's speed. 20 km/h **northwards** is its velocity. Also, speeds are not usually constant so we are finding the average speed over the distance, not the speed at a given instant.

Distance/time graphs

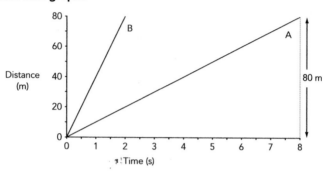

In case A the speed is	$\dfrac{80}{8} = 10$ m/s
A straight line graph shows a	constant speed.
The slope of the line gives the	speed.
The steeper the line	the greater the speed.

Question

Work out the speed for B.

Acceleration

Acceleration is	the rate of change of velocity.
The equation to find acceleration is	Acceleration = $\dfrac{\text{Change in velocity}}{\text{Time taken}}$
The symbol equation is	$a = \dfrac{v - u}{t}$
	v is final velocity, u initial velocity and t the time interval.

The usual unit of acceleration is	metres per second per second.
This is abbreviated to	m/s/s
Speeding up is	positive acceleration.
Slowing down is	negative acceleration (deceleration).

Questions

1   Find the acceleration of the following cars and include the units:

	Initial velocity (m/s)	Final velocity (m/s)	Time taken (s)
a	0	30	10
b	5	25	5
c	30	20	2

2   Which car is:

   i   starting from rest?   ii   slowing down?

Velocity/time graphs

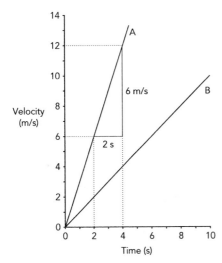

Acceleration of A between 2 s and 4 s

$$= \frac{\text{Change in velocity}}{\text{Time}}$$

$$= \frac{6 \text{ m/s}}{2 \text{ s}}$$

$$= 3 \text{ m/s/s}$$

Distance travelled by A
between 0 s and 4 s

$$= \text{Area under graph}$$

$$= \frac{1}{2} \times 4 \times 12$$

$$= 24 \text{ m}$$

3   Find the acceleration for B between 2 s and 4 s.

4   Find the distance travelled for B between 0 s and 10 s.

Stopping distances

A stopping distance is made up of two parts	distance travelled during reaction time and distance travelled under braking force.

Stopping distance depends on:

the speed of the vehicle because	the faster the vehicle is going the longer it takes to stop.
the driver's reaction time because	it takes time for the nerve impulse to travel from the brain to the foot.
the greater the speed	the further the car travels in the reaction time and the greater the braking time.
the friction between the wheels and the surface because	the greater the friction, the greater the braking force.
the force applied by the braking system because	the greater the force, the shorter the stopping distance.

Ⓠuestion

Complete the following sentences:

A car travelling along a .... road will have a .... stopping distance than if it were on a dry road because there is less .... between the wheels and the .... Friction is a .... which acts when one surface moves against another. It opposes .... Drinking and driving don't go together because alcohol slows the .... time. The .... the reaction time, the greater the distance the car travels before the .... are applied.

Forces in balance

A book resting on a table has two forces acting on it:

A downward force due to	gravity.
An upward force from	the table surface.
The book does not move because	the two forces are in balance.

This means that they are equal in	size.
And they act in the opposite	direction.
The symbol used for force is	F.

> **Hint:** If the forces on a body are balanced, the body will either be at rest or moving at a steady velocity (speed in a given direction). This is Newton's first law of motion. It is easy to think that moving at a steady speed requires a steady force as we often forget about friction.

Unbalanced forces

Unbalanced forces will make a body	speed up
or	slow down
or	change direction.

If a force acts on a body to make it accelerate we know that:

The greater the force,	the greater the acceleration.
The larger the mass,	the smaller the acceleration.
The equation linking these is	Force = mass x acceleration.
The symbol equation for this is	F = m x a
This is called	Newton's second law of motion.

Ⓠuestions

1. a A force of 10 N acts on a mass of 2 kg. What is the resulting acceleration?

   b What would be the acceleration of a 4 kg mass with the same force?

   c What would be the acceleration of a 2 kg mass acted on by a 20 N force?

2. Explain why, when we try to walk on ice, we become aware that friction is useful.

Moments

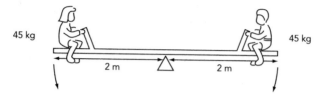

45 kg   2 m   2 m   45 kg

Boy's moment = 45 x 10 x 2 = 900 Nm

A moment is	the turning effect of a force.
The greater the force,	the larger the moment.
The further the distance from the pivot,	the larger the moment.
The equation to remember is	Moment = force x perpendicular distance from the pivot
If there are two equal moments in opposite directions	no turning motion occurs.

Question

a   What is the moment if the boy has a mass of 40 kg and sits at a distance of 1.5 m from the pivot of the seesaw?

b   Where would the girl have to sit now to balance the seesaw?

Gravity and freefall

Acceleration due to gravity

Gravity is a continuous downward force. Therefore bodies accelerate as they fall.

The gravitational field strength is given the symbol	g.
On the surface of the Earth, this is equal to about	10 N/kg (9.8 N/kg more exactly).
On anything falling to Earth, this causes an acceleration of about	10 m/s/s (9.8 m/s/s more exactly).
Weight is a force due to	gravity.
On Earth, the force due to gravity on a mass of m kg is	m x g newtons
m x g is the	weight of a body of mass m kg.

Units: A force of one newton acting on a mass of one kilogram will cause the mass to accelerate at a rate of one metre per second per second.

The gravitational field strength, g, can have units of either N/kg or m/s/s. So g on Earth is given as 10 N/kg or 10 m/s/s. These both mean the same thing: a mass of 1 kg near the Earth feels a force of 10 N. If it is allowed to fall freely, it will accelerate at 10 m/s/s.

Questions

1   Complete the following sentences:

Everything falling freely towards the Earth is .... at about 10 m/s/s. This is because Earth has a .... force field of about 10 N/kg. This should mean that a falling object gets steadily faster and faster but in fact it will reach a steady speed called the .... This is because the air resistance on the falling body gets .... as the speed of the body increases. So, there is a speed at which the downward force due to .... is balanced by the .... force from air resistance. This terminal velocity depends on the .... and size of the falling object. For example, a person's terminal velocity with a parachute is .... than without one. This is because the upward force from air resistance is .... with a parachute.

2   Explain what is happening in each case:

a   A cyclist is travelling along a flat surface. At first her speed increases but she reaches a maximum speed even though she keeps pedalling all the time.

b   A rocket can be fired from Earth and once in space will move at a steady velocity with no further thrust.

3   If an astronaut has a mass of 75 kg, what is his weight on:

a   Earth

b   the Moon?

Take g = 10 m/s/s on Earth and 1.6 m/s/s on the Moon.

Force and pressure on solids

If we stretch a spring (or a wire), there is a pattern to the way it extends:

The greater the load on the spring,	the greater the extension.
For small loads, when the loads are removed	the spring will return to its original shape.
If the elastic limit is exceeded	the spring is permanently changed.

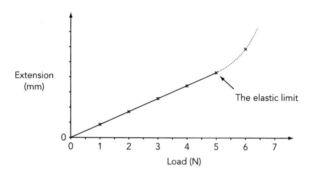

Pressure

Pressure is measured in	pascals.
The abbreviation is	Pa.
One pascal is	1 N/m^2
The greater the force on a given area,	the greater the pressure.
The smaller the area that the force acts on,	the greater the pressure.
Area, force and pressure are connected by the equation	Pressure = force/area

Questions

1   Explain why a tap on the head of a nail will drive the nail into a piece of wood, whereas the same tap on the pointed end will not drive the head of the nail into the wood.

2   The nail has a head of area 10 mm² whereas its point has an area of 0.1 mm². A force of 3000 newtons is used to tap the nail. Work out the pressure applied in each case.

Force and pressure on liquids

The pressure of a liquid increases	with depth.
At any point in a liquid the pressure in all directions	is the same.

Ⓠuestion

Explain why the cross-section of a dam is shaped to have a large base, tapering to a narrow top.

Using pressure exerted by a liquid

Using a liquid in a tube, a force can be applied from a distance and even transmitted round a corner. This is because liquids will transmit or pass on pressure, since the particles of a liquid are so close together.

When liquids are used to transmit forces we call the system	hydraulic.
Hydraulic systems can be used to multiply	forces.
A small force at one end of the system can produce	a large force at the other end.
This is used in	car braking systems and in lifting or crushing machines.

How hydraulic systems work

There are two things to remember:

1 The equation connecting pressure, force and area which is	Pressure = force/area
2 The pressure everywhere in a closed system is	the same.
This means that the value of force/area must be the	same throughout.

A car braking system

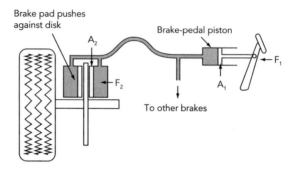

Questions

1 Complete the following sentences:

The pressure P_1 at the small piston of the brake pedal .... the pressure

P_2 at the large piston at the wheel, because .... is the same throughout

a .... system. So $F_1/A_1 =$ .... If A_2 is ten times bigger than

A_1, the force F_2 on the wheel disk must also be .... times bigger than

F_1, the force on the brake .... The advantage of this system is that the

.... force acts on all the wheel disks because the .... is the

same in all directions in an enclosed system.

2

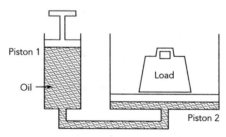

The area of piston 2 is five times that of piston 1. Pressure is applied to the oil by pressing on piston 1.

a How does the pressure on the oil at piston 1 compare with that at piston 2?

b How does the force on piston 2 compare with the force on piston 1? Explain your answer.

Force and pressure on gases

Boyle's Law

For a fixed mass of gas, at constant temperature:

If we increase the pressure on the gas the volume	decreases.
In words, this is	pressure is proportional to 1/volume
In symbols	$P \propto {}^1/_V$
If we change the pressure from P_1 to P_2 and the volume decreases from V_1 to V_2 then	$P_1V_1 = P_2V_2$

> **Hint:** Gas pressure is often measured in atmospheres where 1 atmosphere equals 100 kPa.

Waves

Types of waves

Waves transfer **energy** but not matter.

Light waves and all other electromagnetic waves will pass through a vacuum, but most waves need a material called a medium to pass through. When waves pass through solids, liquids and gases, each particle of the material through which the wave moves is disturbed by moving from its original position and then returning to it. The energy is passed along to the neighbouring particles.

The two kinds of waves are	**transverse** and **longitudinal**.
In a transverse wave, the direction the wave travels is	at right angles to the disturbance.
In a longitudinal wave, the direction the wave travels is	the same direction as the disturbance.

ⓠuestion

Are the following waves transverse or longitudinal?

a   Sound

b   Light

c   Water

d   Along a rope

e   A slinky spring, extended and then released.

Defining waves

The shape of a transverse wave is:

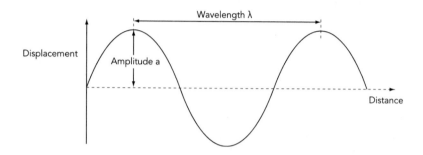

Wavelength has the symbol	λ (pronounced lambda).
It is the distance between two	crests (or troughs) in a transverse wave.
It is measured in	metres, m.
Frequency of a moving wave is the	number of whole waves passing a point per second.
Frequency of a standing wave is	the number of waves (vibrations) produced per second.
Frequency has the symbol	f.
It is measured in	hertz.
The abbreviation for hertz is	Hz.
One hertz is equal to	one vibration per second.

The wave equation

The speed of wave v is equal to	frequency x wavelength
The equation to learn is	$v = f \times \lambda$
The time period, T, of a wave is	the time in seconds for one vibration.
The equation to learn is	frequency = 1/time period

Ｑuestion

Work out the speed of radio waves if the frequency of a radio signal is 200 000 Hz and the wavelength is 1500 m.

Light waves

Light travels in straight lines. The speed at which it travels varies according to the medium through which it passes. Light can be reflected, refracted and diffracted.

White light is composed of several different	colours.
It can be split into these by a	prism.
The colours of the rainbow are	red, orange, yellow, green, blue, indigo, violet.

Hint: **R**ichard **O**f **Y**ork **G**ave **B**attle **I**n **V**ain might help you remember the order of colours in the rainbow.

Reflection

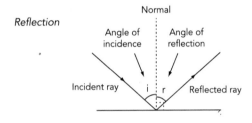

Reflection

The normal is	a line drawn at right angles to a surface such as a mirror.
The angle of incidence is	the angle that the incoming light makes with the normal.
The angle of reflection is	the angle that the reflected ray makes with the normal.
The law of reflection is	Angle of incidence = angle of reflection

Waves

Refraction

Refraction

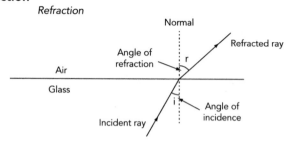

Refraction is the change
of direction when | light waves pass from one medium
to another.

It happens because the speed
at which the wave is travelling | changes.

In a denser medium light travels | slower than in a less dense medium.

When it passes from a denser to a
less dense medium it is refracted | away from the normal.

In glass and other media, the
colours of light travel at | different speeds.

They are therefore refracted by | different amounts.

The slowest light is | violet.

This is refracted by the | largest angle.

Total internal reflection

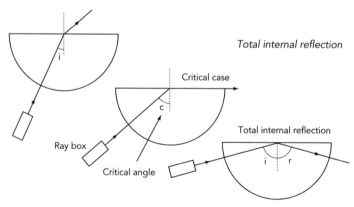

Total internal reflection

ⓠuestions

1   Complete the following sentences:

When light rays are travelling through a dense medium, like glass, they are

.... (or bent) away from the .... when they emerge into a less

dense medium, like air. There is an angle of incidence called the ....

angle at which the ray is refracted along the surface of the glass. At angles of

incidence greater than this it is .... back inside the glass. This is called

.... internal .... It can only happen when rays are travelling

.... a dense .... a less dense material.

2   What type of device is represented in a and b below?

3   Why is total internal reflection important in their use?

Using total internal reflection

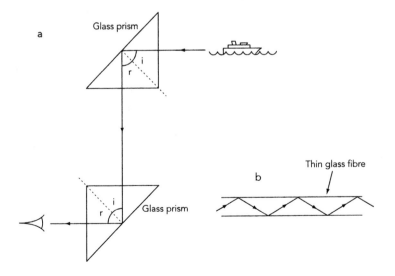

Diffraction

This is the spreading out of waves as | they pass through a small gap or past an obstacle.

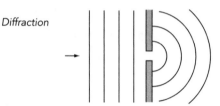

Diffraction

The electromagnetic spectrum

This is a family of energy-carrying waves which have different wavelengths/frequencies.

wavelength (m)

| 10^{-11} | 10^{-10} | 10^{-9} | 10^{-8} | 10^{-7} | 10^{-6} | 10^{-5} | 10^{-4} | 10^{-3} | 10^{-2} | 10^{-1} | 1 | 10^{1} | 10^{2} | 10^{3} |

| Gamma rays | X-rays | Ultraviolet (UV) | V i s i b l e | Infrared (IR) | Radio waves |

Electromagnetic waves can travel through | a vacuum.

They all travel through space at the same | speed.

The waves with the shortest wavelength have the highest | frequencies.

Radio waves have the longest | wavelength.

The waves with the shortest wavelength are | gamma rays.

Visible waves have a wavelength between | infrared and ultraviolet.

Wave	Some uses	Possible dangers
Radio	Broadcasting	
Microwaves	Cooking Satellite transmissions	Living cells damaged by overheating
Infrared	Radiant heaters Grills and toasters TV remote controls Night vision cameras	Skin may burn
Visible	Optical fibres	
Ultraviolet	Sun beds Viewing security-coded equipment	Below-skin tissue damage. Blindness. Normal cells may become cancerous
X-rays	Shadow photography to show internal structures such as bones or metals	Cell damage, normal cells may become cancerous
Gamma	Sterilising food and medical equipment Cancer treatment	Cell damage, normal cells may become cancerous

Sound

Sound waves are carried by the vibration of particles and so sound will not travel through a vacuum. Sound waves are longitudinal. The waves can be reflected, refracted and diffracted.

The louder the sound, the bigger the	amplitude.
The higher the pitch of the note, the bigger	the frequency.
Sound waves travel through different media at different	speeds.
The more dense the medium that the sound passes through	the faster the speed.
An echo is	a reflection of a sound wave.
We can hear sounds round corners because sound waves are	diffracted.

Ⓠuestion

The wave traces i, ii, iii of different sounds were obtained by using a cathode ray oscilloscope.

a   Which two are of the same loudness?

b   Which has the highest note?

c   Which has the lowest note?

Ultrasound waves

These are waves which have a frequency	higher than our audible frequency range.
They are used in hospitals for	finding an image of a baby in the womb.
They are used in industry for	cleaning and quality control.
They are used at sea for	finding the depth of water.
Bats use them for	finding their way by echo location.

Ultrasonic waves are partly reflected when they meet a boundary between two different media. The further away the boundary is, the longer it takes for the reflected sound to reach a detector. The information is converted to a visual display for foetal scans or to detect flaws in metal casings.

Problems with sound

Our ears can hear frequencies between about	20 and 20 000 Hz.
The upper limit declines with	increasing age.
Excessively loud sound can cause	damage to hearing.
This can be produced by	personal stereos, discos, machinery.
Noise levels can be reduced by	sound-absorbing materials.

Shock waves

Earthquakes produce shock waves which travel through the Earth and can be used to provide information about the Earth's structure.

The two types of shock waves are	P-waves and S-waves.
P-waves travel through	solids and liquids.
P-waves are	longitudinal.
S-waves travel through	solids only.
S-waves are	transverse.
The speed of P-waves is	greater than S-waves.
Both waves travel faster through	denser material.
When they reach a change in density they are	refracted.

The Earth's structure

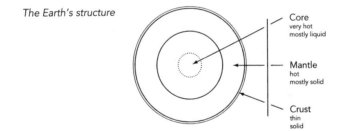

Core
very hot
mostly liquid

Mantle
hot
mostly solid

Crust
thin
solid

Question

What sort of waves would be received at stations A, B and C, and why?

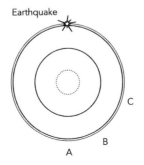

Earthquake

The Earth and beyond

The solar system

The solar system consists of:	Sun, Mercury, Venus, Earth, Mars, (asteroids), Jupiter, Saturn, Uranus, Neptune, Pluto

> **Hint: S**on – **M**y **V**ery **E**arthy **M**ars **J**ust **S**ent **U**ncle **N**eptune **P**otty
> (or make up your own)

The Sun is a	star.
It is made of	gas.
Stars are sources of	light and other forms of electromagnetic energy.
Stars are orbited by	planets.
A planet does not give out	light.
A moon is a body that	orbits a planet.
The nearest planet to the Sun is	Mercury.
The asteroids are	a group of rocks orbiting the Sun.
They lie between	the orbits of Mars and Jupiter.
All the planets in our system orbit	the Sun.
Their orbits are in the same	plane (apart from Pluto).
A comet orbits our Sun in a different	plane from the other planets.
The furthest planet from our Sun is	Pluto.
We see stars because	they give out light.
We see planets and moons because	they reflect the Sun's light.
If we look out at the stars they seem to	move round the Earth.
This is because the	Earth is rotating.
The Earth rotates on its axis every	24 hours.
Where it faces the Sun we have	daylight.

Night-time occurs where	the Earth is not facing the Sun.
The Earth travels round the Sun in	one year.
The Moon travels round the Earth in	one month.

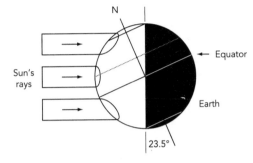

Sunlight falling on the Earth

Sun's rays

N

Equator

Earth

23.5°

Question

Complete the following sentences:

The equator divides the Earth into two hemispheres – the Northern and the

.... The Earth is tilted on its .... This means that the Northern

hemisphere has the season .... when it is tilted away from the Sun. At this

time the Southern hemisphere has .... In winter, the days are ....

than in summer, and the Sun's rays are spread over a greater area.

Gravitational forces

It isn't just the Earth that has a gravitational pull. Anything with mass attracts every other mass. The force of attraction is called gravity.

The bigger the mass,	the bigger its force of gravity.
The further away from the mass,	the smaller its force of gravity.

The inverse square law

The distance, d, between masses, m_1 and m_2, makes a very big difference. The gravitational force is proportional to the inverse square of the distance, ie $F \propto 1/d^2$.

The equation to remember is	$$F = \frac{G\,m_1 m_2}{d^2}$$ (where G is the gravitational constant)
Work through the following:	
A body of mass 1 kg on the Earth's surface has a weight of	10 N
If this same body moves twice as far away from the centre of the Earth, its weight is	$$\frac{10}{2^2} = 2.5 \text{ N}$$
This is because	the distance has doubled, so the force (the weight) is a quarter of 10 N.

Question

Find the weight of the 1 kg mass if it moves out to:

a   3 Earth radii

b   4 Earth radii.

Artificial satellites

Artificial satellites are sent into orbit round the Earth to	monitor the weather
	send information between places on Earth
	observe the universe
The further away the satellite, the longer it takes to	orbit the Earth.

Question

Complete the following sentences:

Communication satellites usually orbit the .... at a particular distance from
the Earth. They move round the Earth at exactly the same rate as the Earth spins.
They are therefore always in the .... position in the sky when viewed from
Earth. Satellites which monitor the weather are usually put into a lower orbit round
the .... In this way the Earth spins beneath them and they can scan the
whole Earth every day.

The universe

The universe is made up of at least a billion	galaxies.
A galaxy is a collection of millions of	stars.
Our galaxy is called	the Milky Way.
A light year is	the distance travelled by light in one Earth year.
So, a light year is a measure of	distance.

How did the universe start?

We believe the beginning of the universe is explained by	the Big Bang theory.
This says	the universe began with an explosion and has been expanding outwards ever since.

Evidence: Red shifts

This is the effect which causes	the light from all other galaxies to be shifted into the red end of the electromagnetic spectrum.
The greater the red shift,	the further away the galaxy.
A shift to the red means that	the galaxies are moving away from us.
The faster a galaxy is moving away,	the greater the red shift.
The galaxies farthest away from us are moving away	fastest.

163

Another theory, the **steady state theory**, says that matter is constantly being created.

The life of a star

A star begins to form when	large swirls of dust and gas (nebulae) collapse inward.
When it is dense enough, the core becomes hot enough for	nuclear reactions to take place.
The temperature is so hot that	electrons are stripped from the hydrogen atoms.
The hydrogen nuclei are fused together to produce	helium nuclei.
This results in	lots of energy being given out, as some mass is converted to energy.
This outward radiation of energy opposes	the inward pull of gravity.
This continues until	the star runs out of fuel.
The next stage is that the star	swells to become a red giant, losing gas and dust to space.
The last stage for medium-sized stars is that	they form white dwarf stars.
Giant stars have a different ending	the red supergiant blows up.
This huge explosion is called	a supernova.
It leaves behind	a small neutron star surrounded by an expanding nebula of dust and gas.

Second generation stars: New stars can form from the dust and gas cloud from a supernova. Our Sun was formed in this way. The Sun and its planets contain heavy elements, which were made in first generation stars.

Questions

1 What is the name for the gas and dust clouds from which stars are made?

2 What makes the clouds:

   a   collapse inward   b   get hot?

Energy resources and energy transfer

Energy sources

There are many different forms of energy.

A fuel stores	chemical energy.
A washing machine is driven by	electrical energy.
A fire gives out	heat (thermal) energy.
Movement is an example of	kinetic energy.
A catapult uses	elastic or strain energy.
A man up a ladder has gained	gravitational potential energy.
A microwave oven uses	microwave radiation to rotate water particles.
Potential energy is the general name for	stored energy.

Ⓠuestion

Name three other sources of energy.

Energy transfer

Heat

The hotness of a body is called its	temperature.
Temperature is measured in	degrees Celsius °C (sometimes called degrees centigrade).
A hot body will transfer heat energy only to	a colder body.
The unit of energy is	the joule.
This has the symbol	J.
The three ways that heat energy can travel are	convection, conduction, radiation.

Conduction

Conduction occurs best in	solids and liquids.
Heat travels by means of	vibrating particles.

Metals are	good conductors.
Non-metals are	poor conductors or insulators.
Trapped air is one of the best	insulators.

Question

Why would gases be rather poor conductors of heat?

Convection

Convection occurs in	fluids (gases and liquids).
The heat is carried by	moving particles.
A convection current in air can be described as	cold air sinking and hot air rising.
Hot air rises because	it is less dense than cold air.
This is because the hotter the air,	the further apart the particles.

Question

What is the basic difference between conduction and convection?

Radiation

Unlike conduction and convection, radiation can occur in	a vacuum.
This means that it doesn't need the presence of	particles.
The Earth receives radiant heat through space from	the Sun.
The hotter the body	the greater the radiant heat it gives out.
A black body is	a good radiator (loses heat quickly).
It is also a	good heat absorber (heats up quickly).
A shiny body is	a poor radiator and a poor absorber of heat.
Heat is often called	infrared radiation.
At a shiny surface it is	reflected.

Questions

1 If hot water is poured into a black beaker and a silver beaker, which would cool faster and why?

2 Complete the following sentences:

A .... surface does not absorb as much heat as a dull surface. This is

because some of the heat is .... Infrared radiation behaves like light

in this way, because it is a type of .... radiation. Light colours are

.... at absorbing heat than dark colours. In general, surfaces that are

good absorbers of heat are also .... emitters when hot.

A greenhouse and the greenhouse effect: The Sun radiates light and mostly high-energy short-wave infrared radiation. This passes through the glass in a greenhouse. The heat is absorbed by the soil and the plants and this raises their temperature. They then radiate heat but it is infrared with a **longer** wavelength and will not pass through glass. So the temperature in the greenhouse rises. Carbon dioxide in the atmosphere has the same effect as the glass in a greenhouse.

Question

Explain how the Earth is heating up.

Evaporation

Evaporation is also a way to transfer energy.

Evaporation is	the gradual loss of particles from the surface of a liquid.
Particles which escape from the surface of a liquid have	the highest energy.

The rate of evaporation of water:

the larger the surface area of the water	the faster the rate.
the more humidity in the atmosphere	the slower the rate.
the more air movement around the surface	the faster the rate.
the hotter the temperature	the faster the rate.

Questions

1 Complete the following sentences:

   If something is .... than its surroundings it will lose heat until it reaches

   the same temperature. Insulation is used to .... down this process.

   Many forms of insulation involve trapped .... as the insulator. This is

   why it is good to wear several .... of clothing to keep warm. Cavity

   walls are often filled with foam, and the foam itself traps .... A thick

   layer of a particular material is .... than a thin layer. Double glazing is

   made up of two panes of glass with a thin layer of air between them. The air is a

   good .... currents cannot form between the glass panes

   because the air gap is too narrow.

2 Explain how the vacuum flask is designed to reduce heat loss.

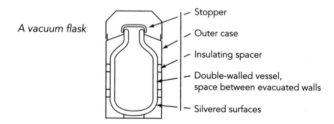

A vacuum flask

- Stopper
- Outer case
- Insulating spacer
- Double-walled vessel, space between evacuated walls
- Silvered surfaces

The efficiency of energy transfers

Energy can never be created or destroyed. However, as we use (transfer) it we can never transfer all the energy we started with into the new form we want. Some is always lost, usually as heat energy. The more stages there are, the greater the inefficiency.

The equation to remember is

$$\text{Efficiency} = \frac{\text{Useful energy output}}{\text{Total energy input}} \times 100\%$$

Questions

1 Describe the type of energy transfer when a car is driven along a road. How is energy lost to the system?

2 If 15 000 joules of chemical energy from the fuel is put in to achieve 5000 joules of kinetic energy, what is the efficiency of the energy transfer in the car?

Work

Work is done whenever energy is transferred. The units of work are therefore joules.

Energy transferred (J) = Work done (J)

The equation for measuring work done is:

Work done = Force (newtons) x distance moved in the direction of the force (metres)

This is abbreviated to $\qquad$ W = F x d

Power

Power is	the rate of doing work.
The unit of power is	the watt.
This has the symbol	W.
The equation is	$\text{Power} = \dfrac{\text{Work done (joules)}}{\text{Time taken (seconds)}}$
This is abbreviated to	$P = \dfrac{F \times d}{t}$

Questions

1 What is the work done when a load of mass 100 kg is lifted onto a bench 2 m above the ground?

2 A girl can lift 120 1 kg bags of sugar onto a shelf of height 2 m in 1 minute. What is her power?

Kinetic energy

Kinetic energy is the energy of	motion.
The equation to remember is	Kinetic energy = $\frac{1}{2} mv^2$
In this equation m stands for	mass of the moving object.
v stands for	its velocity.

Gravitational potential energy

Gravitational potential energy is energy due to	position.
The equation to remember is	gravitational energy = mgh
In this equation m stands for	mass of the object.
g stands for	acceleration due to gravity (or gravitational field strength).

| On Earth this is approximately | 10 m/s/s |
| In this equation h stands for | height in metres. |

ⓠuestion

How much gravitational potential energy does a suitcase of mass 30 kg have when it is on the third floor, 10 m above the ground?

Radioactivity

Radioactivity is an emission of energy from the nuclei of chemical elements. The rate at which this occurs cannot be changed by physical or chemical means.

It results from the breakdown of	atomic nuclei.
It can be detected by	a Geiger-Müller (G-M) tube or a photographic plate.
The radioactivity that is always around is called	**background radiation**.
Some sources of this are	rocks, radiation from space, the air.

Alpha, beta and gamma radiation

| The three types of emission are | alpha particles, beta particles and gamma rays. |
| When radioactive elements decay a new | element is formed (sometimes also radioactive). |

Alpha (α) particles

In air, alpha particles only travel	a few centimetres.
They are absorbed by	paper.
They are composed of	helium nuclei.
They are formed when	a nucleus ejects a group of two protons and two neutrons.
They have the symbol	^4_2He
They have a charge of	+2
They have a relative atomic mass of	4

Beta (β) particles

In air, beta particles can travel	several centimetres (depending on their speed).
They are stopped by	thin aluminium.
They are composed of	fast-moving electrons.
These are formed when	a neutron in the nucleus turns into a proton and an electron.
They have the symbol	$^{0}_{1}e$
They have a charge of	−1
They have almost no	mass.

Gamma (γ) radiation

In air, gamma radiation can travel	long distances.
It is stopped by	thick concrete or several centimetres of lead.
It has no	charge or mass.
It is part of the	electromagnetic spectrum (like light).
The frequency of the radiation is	very high.
The wavelength of the radiation is	very short.

Half-life

This is the time taken for half a given number of radioactive atoms to decay to different atoms. It is usually measured by finding the time taken for a radioactive count at any point to drop to half. You will often have to plot a graph and find the half-life from the graph.

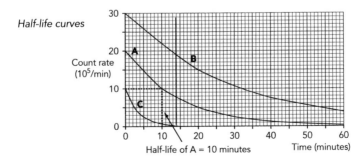

Half-life curves

Half-life of A = 10 minutes

Question

Find the half lives of B and C.

The radioactivity of any element decreases with	time.
The radioactive count could be measured with	a Geiger-Müller tube.
A short half-life means that it decays	quickly.

Questions

1

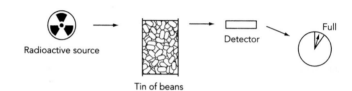

Radioactive source

Tin of beans

Detector

Full

If you wanted to measure the fill level of a tin of beans using radioactive monitoring, which kind of radioactive emission would be suitable and why? What sort of half-life would be most suitable?

2   An oil company is looking for the source of a leak in its underground pipeline. Some radioactive material was added to the oil. What sort of:

a   radioactive emission and

b   half-life, would be best?

Effects of radiation

Radioactive emissions can cause cell damage and cancer and even cell death if the dose is large enough. Radioactive emissions are called ionising radiation because the radiation has enough energy to knock electrons from atoms to form ions. In doing so it alters the cell chemistry.

Precautions with radioactive substances

Radioactive material should be handled at	a distance.
The handler should wear	protective clothing.
The level of exposure may be measured by wearing	a photographic plate badge.
Inside the body, the most dangerous radiation is	alpha.

This is because	it is the most ionising as it has the largest mass and can do most damage at a short range.
Outside the body, the most danger comes from	beta or gamma radiation.
This is because	these types of radiation will pass through the skin and damage the cells.

Uses of radioactivity

Radioactivity is used in industry for tracing and quality control.

Tracing is	adding a radioactive material and monitoring where it goes.
Quality control uses	penetrating radioactive beams to measure thickness or fill levels.
Radioactivity is used in the medical world for	treating cancers (cancer cells are less resistant to radioactivity than healthy cells)
	tracing (for example, radioactive iodine to check the activity of the thyroid gland).

Dating rocks

Igneous rocks start out with a proportion of	uranium, a radioactive element.
This eventually decays to	lead.
The older the rock,	the more lead and the less uranium.

Carbon dating

All living material contains a fixed proportion of	radioactive carbon (carbon-14).
When the material dies	the radioactive carbon breaks down, and is not replaced.
The older the material,	the less radioactive carbon is present.

Question

The carbon in living wood has a count rate of 16 counts per minute per gram. The half-life of carbon-14 is 6000 years. A small sample of wood of mass 1 g has a count rate of 2 counts per minute. How old is the wood?

Radioactivity

Nuclear reactors

Nuclear reactors use a process called	nuclear fission.
An element such as uranium is bombarded with	neutrons.
The uranium nucleus	splits into two.
This releases more	neutrons.
These neutrons	cause further uranium atoms to break up.
This is called a	**chain reaction**.
The amount of energy released is	very large.
Environmental problems include	storage and disposal of radioactive waste accidental releases of radioactive material.

174

Answers

Life Processes and Living Things

Page 2

Cells, cell membrane, cytoplasm, nucleus, cell membrane, selectively-permeable, cell wall, permeable, chlorophyll, absorbs, sap vacuoles.

Page 3

Sperm has a tail so it can swim towards an egg in order for fertilisation to take place. It contains only half the number of chromosomes of its parent so that on fusion with an egg the full number is made up.

Palisade leaf cells have many chloroplasts because most of the plant's photosynthesis occurs in them. They are shaped so that the light enters the cell through the short side so that little is absorbed by the cell wall.

Page 4

a	Organ	b	Organelle
c	Cell	d	Organism
e	Organelle	f	Cell and organism.

Page 6

1   Diffusion is the random spreading out of particles which happens whenever there are moving particles. Osmosis is the movement of water only (by diffusion) across a selectively-permeable membrane.

2   Selectively-permeable membrane, from, to, more, more.

Pages 9 and 10

1   a   Enzymes are proteins which are biological catalysts, which means that they speed up chemical reactions but are not themselves changed. Each enzyme is specific for a particular reaction.

b   They help to break down food into chemicals that are small and soluble and can pass into the bloodstream.

c   Amylase breaks down starch into glucose. Proteases break down proteins to amino acids. Lipase breaks down fats into fatty acids.

2   Tube, taking, breaking, villi, ileum, small, large, colon, rectum, water, salts, egestion.

Page 11

1   Cardiac muscle.

2   Because they have to pump the blood to other parts of the body, whereas the atria just receive blood.

3   The left ventricle is thicker because it must pump blood to the whole body, whereas the right ventricle pumps blood only to the nearby lungs.
    [Hint: **Thick left** ventricle = tickle]

4

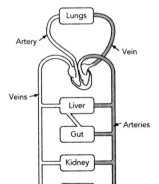

Oxygenated blood shaded

5   To make sure the blood flows in one direction only.

Answers

Page 13

1 Oxygenated, oxygen, deoxygenated, right, right, lungs, valves, muscles, capillaries, oxygen, carbon dioxide.

2 a Capillaries are the network of tiny blood vessels which link arteries to veins. They provide an area where tissue fluid (plasma) leaks out to bathe the cells so that the cells can extract from it for their needs and excrete into it their waste products.

   b i branching means that the surface area is increased

     ii very thin-walled means that gas exchange is fast

     iii narrow means blood flow is slowed down to allow exchange.

Page 14

1 a Blood carries (or transports):
- oxygen to cells and carbon dioxide from cells
- digested food to cells
- urea made in the liver to the kidneys
- hormones all over the body
- heat.

   b It stops bleeding by clotting at injured site. It fights diseases by producing antibodies or by engulfing bacteria.

2 Marrow, nucleus, haemoglobin, red, iron, oxyhaemoglobin, colour, arterial, arterial, blue-red.

Page 18

1 Large surface area for diffusion to take place on a large scale; Moist surface so that gases can dissolve for diffusion; Plentiful blood supply because gases must diffuse in and out of the blood; Thin surface so that gases can diffuse through quickly.

2 Both result in the release of energy from glucose.
Aerobic respiration produces more energy than anaerobic respiration and requires oxygen as a reactant. It produces carbon dioxide and water as waste products.
Anaerobic respiration has different waste products: lactic acid from muscles, or alcohol and carbon dioxide from fermentation.

3 Oxygen, carbon dioxide, exchange, respiratory, respiration, breathing, inspiration, increases, lungs.

Page 20

1 a They have a nucleus, a cell membrane and are filled with cytoplasm.

   b They have nerve fibres made of cytoplasm and a long axon to transmit nerve impulses. They have a myelin sheath that insulates the nerve fibres so that the electrical messages travel quickly.

2 a The reflex arc misses out the brain so that the stimulus is immediately responded to in the spinal column by the spinal nerves. This allows a much quicker response, which is important when we wish to avoid dangerous situations.

   b Some examples of this in action – escape from sudden pain such as touching a hot plate or treading on a sharp point, or anticipation of pain, eye-blinking to avoid damage, ducking to avoid a blow, etc.

   c If the painful stimuli is dealt with by a reflex action, the brain receives the message from the site after the muscles have responded.

Page 23

1 Radials, circulars, circulars, pupil, less, relaxed, larger, light.

2 a Light passes through the transparent cornea which bends the rays into the lens. The lens remains flat, so that the rays bend only slightly to be focused onto the back of the retina.

b When the object is close up, the rays of light from the object will need to be bent more as they will be diverging when they enter the eye. The cornea bends the rays in the same way as before, but the lens will bulge, so that it will bend the rays to a greater extent.

3 Ciliary, flat, relaxed, suspensory ligaments, lens.

Page 27

A Menstruation – the thick lining of the uterus and the unfertilised egg pass out through the vagina.

B represents the time when the lining of the uterus thickens ready to receive the embryo. A follicle develops inside the ovary.

C is the time of ovulation, ie when an ovum is released from the follicle. The corpus luteum releases progesterone which keeps the lining thick.

D The lining remains thick awaiting fertilisation of the egg. With no fertilisation, the corpus luteum dies.

Page 28

Insulin, pancreas, rises, liver, glycogen, diabetes, carbohydrate, glucose, glycogen, low.

Page 32

1 Blood is filtered by the Bowman's capsule. This means that although proteins and blood cells stay in the blood, other valuable substances, such as amino acids and glucose, pass into the kidney, along with unwanted urea. These substances are reabsorbed back into the blood by blood capillaries that wrap around the nephrons. Water may also be reabsorbed here.

2 Excretory, artery, blood, medulla, ureter, pelvis, urine, bladder, vein.

Page 33

1 Labels clockwise from top left: Dead cells, Hair follicle, Sebaceous gland, Sweat gland, Erector muscle.

2 Our muscles generate heat by the process of respiration. As they are working harder than usual, they generate more heat than usual.

3 We rely on sweating to cool down, when the water from sweat evaporates from our skin into the air. It is more difficult for this to happen when the air itself is moist.

4 Still air is a very good insulator. More of this is trapped between layers than is held by a single thick layer.

5 Temperature, sweat, body, capillaries, dilate, heat, contract, air, fat, insulator.

Page 36

1 The skin bleeds to wash microbes away and forms a clot to seal the wound. White cells (phagocytes) in the blood engulf the invading microbes, but if they still survive, more white cells (lymphocytes) make chemicals called antibodies which are designed to kill off the microbes. If they still survive, the body has signs of the disease until these mechanisms work. Any toxins produced by the bacteria are neutralised by white cells which produce antitoxins.
Once antibodies for a particular disease are in the blood, the body is usually immune to the disease because if it reappears in the blood stream the antibodies can be made quickly and in large numbers.

2 Cancer, cilia, bronchitis, oxygen, nicotine, addictive, young, older.

Answers

1   The plant needs light for photosynthesis and the larger the surface area, the more light it can absorb. The plant uses carbon dioxide for photosynthesis and as there is only a tiny percentage in the air, the large surface area provides the best chance of obtaining it.

2   They have the function of protecting the leaves, but to allow light through to the other cells within the leaves they are transparent and have no chloroplasts.

Page 39

1   They do not move because they make their own food by photosynthesis.

2   Plants need energy for growth and reproduction and for transporting food to cells. They get it by respiration.

3   Oxygen diffuses into all parts of the plant and dissolves in the thin layer of moisture round the cells.

4   Photosynthesis, water, carbon dioxide, glucose, oxygen, light, light, respiration, water, carbon dioxide, photosynthesis, respiration, oxygen, carbon dioxide, respiration, oxygen, carbon dioxide.

Page 41

a   If light increases, photosynthesis increases. This uses water so the overall effect will be to slow transpiration.

b   If wind increases, water given out at the leaf surface will be blown away so the air around the leaf surface will not be saturated and transpiration will increase.

c   If temperature increases, the air will be able to hold more water, so more will evaporate, so transpiration will increase.

d   If the air becomes more humid, it will contain more water, less water will be able to evaporate, so transpiration will decrease.

Page 43

1   A tropism is the growth in a particular direction that plants make as a response to a stimulus.

2   Plants are able to make the most of their surroundings. Shoots grow towards light which means they have the best conditions for photosynthesis. Roots grow downwards under the influence of gravity, which allows them to find water under the ground and to anchor the plant firmly.

Page 44

a   Genetics   b   Both

c   Both   d   Genetics

e   Environment.

Page 47

The offspring of sexual reproduction have $1/2$ their chromosomes from one parent and $1/2$ from the other. The genotype of any offspring is a random combination of genes from the two parents, so the offspring will all be different.

Page 48

Exactly one half the sperm are X (which will produce a girl on fertilisation) and the other half are Y (which will produce a boy on fertilisation).

Page 49

1   25%

Gamete from male

		F	f
Gamete from female	F	FF	Ff
	f	Ff	ff

2   a   Jane, because she is the only one with two recessive genes.

b   No, because any child must receive a dominant gene from her.

Page 50

1   TT = tall and tt = short

2   F_1 generation

Tall gamete

		T	T
Short gamete	t	Tt	Tt
	t	Tt	Tt

3 Tall is dominant because all the offspring were tall.

4 F$_2$ generation

	T	t
T	TT	Tt
t	Tt	tt

Only tt plant will be short as the T gene is dominant

Pages 51 and 52

1 The light-coloured moths, whose camouflage is ineffective, get eaten more and decrease in numbers. The dark-coloured moths are well camouflaged so get eaten less often than they would be on light-coloured trees. Over a period of time, this means that they and their eggs survive. Their numbers gradually increase.

2 Vehicle exhausts and industrial pollution produce sooty deposits.

3 The light-coloured moth would increase in numbers as it would become the better camouflaged version.

Page 53

a Camels have large feet so they don't sink into the sand. They store water and fat in their hump. Their eyes are protected from sand by a third eyelid and long eyelashes.

b Desert cacti have tiny leaves (their spines) to reduce the rate of transpiration. Their large, fleshy shape stores water. They have long roots to find water.

Page 56

1 a There are many different habitats in a large forest, some of which might only exist in a particular place. When the forest is chopped down most of these habitats will be lost. Sometimes this means the loss of a whole species of animal.

b A lot of rainfall may be caught by the leaves of trees, as well as being absorbed by their roots. This water

would all be dumped directly onto the land if the trees were cut down. The rush of water to the rivers would take the top soil with it and the soil would gradually erode.

2 Warm, heat, space, fossil, carbon dioxide, methane, temperature, rising, level, expands, ice.

Page 57

1

Leaves
Producers

↓

Worms
Primary consumers
Herbivores

↓

Moles
Secondary consumers
Carnivores

↓

Foxes
Tertiary consumers
Carnivores

2 a The gull population would increase because the competition for food from the small fish is removed.

b The tern population would decrease because some of their food supply has gone.

Page 58

1

Pyramid of biomass

Fleas
Dog

Pyramid of number

Fleas
Dog

2 Energy is never transferred efficiently (ie completely). Since each layer depends on the one below it for its existence, the mass of each layer must go down as the available energy goes down.

Materials and their Properties

1 Three, solid, liquid, gas, fixed, gas, fast, liquid, liquids, slowly, gases.

2 a The solid turns into a liquid at the melting point because the particles have enough energy to move from their fixed vibrating positions in the solid into the random movement of a liquid.

b The particles move faster and more freely with a greater distance between them.

3 Pressure is caused by the particles bombarding the sides of a container. If the temperature goes down, the gas particles are moving less rapidly and with less energy, so there will be fewer, less energetic collisions with the sides.

Page 67

1 a Mg 12 p, 12 n, 12 e

b F 9 p, 10 n, 9 e

c K 19 p, 20 n, 19 e.

2 A 8 n, 8 e

B A = 9, 4 e

C 13 p, 14 n

D 1 p, 0 n, 1 e.

Page 68

a $^{20}_{10}$Ne 10 p 10 e 10 n
$^{22}_{10}$Ne 10 p 10 e 12 n

b A_r = ((90x20) + (10x22)) ÷ 100
= (1800 + 220) ÷ 100= 20.2

Page 70

2 a i 3

ii Group 1 (it has one electron in its outer shell)

iii metal (it has one electron in its outer shell)

b i 17

ii Group VII (it has seven electrons in its outer shell)

iii metal (it has 7 electrons in its outer shell)

c i 7

ii Group V (it has five electrons in its outer shell)

iii non-metal (it has five electrons in its outer shell)

Page 72

1 a Covalent (non-metal with non-metal)

b Ionic (metal with non-metal)

c Covalent (non-metal with non-metal)

d Metallic (metal only)

2 a

2 pairs of shared electrons

Oxygen molecule, formula O_2

b

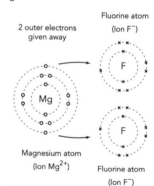

2 outer electrons given away

Fluorine atom (Ion F$^-$)

Magnesium atom (Ion Mg^{2+})

Fluorine atom (Ion F$^-$)

Answers

Page 74

1. W molecular covalent
   X giant covalent
   Y giant ionic
   Z giant metallic
2. a Z – metals conduct well as solids and liquids
   b X – high melting point means giant and covalently bonded structures never conduct
   c W – low melting point means molecular structure which must be covalent
   d Y – This is ionic (metal/non-metal) as it conducts poorly as a solid and well as a liquid. All ionically bonded structures are giant.
3. Non-metal, ion, negative, non-metals, giant, high, melted (or liquid), molecular, molecular, conduct electricity.

Page 75

a $Ca(OH)_2$
b Na_2SO_4
c $CaCO_3$

Page 77

a Magnesium sulphate
b Magnesium nitrate
c Hydrochloric acid
d Calcium carbonate
e Sulphuric acid.

Page 80

Mixture, heating, molecules, petrol, polyethene (or polythene), physical, chemical.

Page 84

Carbon dioxide, water, oxygen, monoxide, greenhouse effect, acid rain, sulphur dioxide.

Page 85

Positively, cathode, electrolyte.

Page 87

1. a This is a list of metals in order of their reactivity, with the most reactive metals at the top.
   b It allows us to predict the reactions of metals.
2. a Zinc oxide
   b Sodium hydroxide
   c Iron chloride
   d Aluminium sulphate + hydrogen
   e Magnesium oxide + zinc
   f Copper sulphate, zinc (sulphate).

Page 90

Coke, limestone, monoxide, slag.

Page 92

$NH_3 + HNO_3 \longrightarrow NH_4NO_3$

Page 94 (top)

a 2 Na, 1 C, 3 O
b 3N, 12H, 1P, 4 O

Page 94 (bottom)

a 80   b 98
c 74

Page 95

a $^{64}/_{80}$ x100 = 80%
b $^{40}/_{74}$ x 100 = 54%

Page 96

CH_4

Page 97

a 0.0025
b 0.08 g

Page 98

Carbon dioxide, cooled, plant, oceans, oxygen, radiation, animal, carbon dioxide, 20, 80.

Page 101

Igneous, magma, large, sedimentary, fossils, pressure.

Answers

Page 103

A   will have small crystals which may even be glassy because molten rock will cool quickly at the surface, eg basalt.

B   will have large crystals because the molten rock will cool slowly under the surface, eg granite.

C   will be metamorphosed by the heat of the magma and the pressure of deep burial, eg marble.

Pages 104 and 105

1   Transition metals

2   Alkali metals

3   Metals

4   Non-metals

5   Halogens

Page 108

A   Chlorine

B   Hydrogen

C   Sodium hydroxide

D   Anode

E   Cathode

Page 114

Energy put in to break bonds is +3758 kJ/mol.

Energy given out on making bond is –5076 kJ/mol.

ΔH = –1318 kJ/mol, exothermic.

Physical Processes

Page 118

1   Voltage, larger, smaller.

2   a   i   ii

Parallel   Series

   b   i   ii

3   a   2 A

   b   i   1 A

       ii   3 A

   c   i   4 A

       ii   2 A

       iii   4 A

Page 119

Wire, length, longer, decreases.

Page 120

1   a   2 V

   b   10 V

   c   Both 2 V.

2

Page 121

1   I = V/R

2   a   5 Ω

   b   3 Ω.

Page 124

a   5 A

b   13 A

Page 126

Different, same, magnetised, search, current, melt, rating.

Page 128

1 Cold water enters at the bottom.
2 The tank is lagged to reduce heat loss.
3 The water is hottest at the top.
4 Hot water rises by convection currents.

Page 129

1 1 kW x 5 h = 5 kW h
5 x 7 = 35p
2 0.6 kW x $^2/_{60}$ h
= $^{0.6}/_{30}$ kW h
$^{0.6}/_{30}$ x 8 = 0.16p

Page 130

a b

Page 131

Rub, charge, lightning, joules, tall, metal, ground, pointed, opposite.

Page 132 (middle)

Increases, larger.

Page 132 (bottom)

1 a 120 C   b 720 C
c 18 000 C
2 c

Page 133

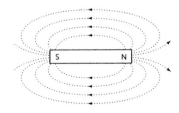

Page 134

North, south, corkscrew, clockwise.

Page 135

Current, electromagnet, armature, striker, magnet.

Page 137

1 Magnetic field, magnets, current, downward, turn, commutator, same.
2 Carbon conducts electricity, doesn't corrode and is self-lubricating (slippery).

Page 139

1 $\dfrac{N_2}{N_1} = \dfrac{V_2}{V_1}$

$\dfrac{N_2}{1000} = \dfrac{12}{240}$

$N_2 = 50$ turns
2 a 480 V   b 80 V
c 5 V.
3 Lower, input, fewer, primary, alternating.

Page 140

a So that the energy loss is minimised because a high voltage allows a low current and the lower the current, the smaller the heat loss.
b So that it can be stepped-up and down using transformers.

Page 141

1 a 100 N
b 0.1 N (Did you remember to convert to kilograms by dividing by 1000?)
c 1 N.
2 a 100 miles/hour
b 50 km/hour
c 2 m/s
d 400 cm/s.

Page 142

40 m/s

Page 143

1 a 3 m/s/s   b 4 m/s/s
c −5 m/s/s
2 i a   ii c

Answers

3   1 m/s/s

4   50 m

Page 144

Wet, longer, friction, ground, force, movement (or motion), reaction, longer, brakes.

Page 145

1   a   5 m/s/s

   b   2.5 m/s/s

   c   10 m/s/s

2   There is so little friction between our shoe and the ice that we cannot push off from the ground.

Page 146

a 600 Nm, b 1.33 m from pivot.

Page 147

1   Accelerating, gravitational, terminal velocity, larger, gravity, upward, shape, smaller (or slower), larger.

2   a   The cyclist has two frictional forces acting against the force which causes forward motion: friction between the wheels and the ground, and air resistance.

      Air resistance is the important one because it increases with speed. The cyclist reaches a speed where the air resistance increases such that it cancels out the pedalling force. She then travels at a steady speed.

   b   The rocket on the other hand, only receives one thrust, but once the rocket has left the atmosphere there is no air resistance, and it will continue to move at a steady velocity, ie speed in the same direction, unless another force acts upon it.

3   a   Weight on Earth is
75 kg x 10 m/s/s = 750 N

   b   Weight on the Moon is
75 kg x 1.6 m/s/s = 120 N.
Note that kg m/s/s = N

Page 148

1   The point of a nail has a very small area resulting in a very high pressure. The head of a nail has a larger area resulting in a smaller pressure.

2   Pressure on head = 300 000 000 Pa
Pressure on point = 30 000 000 000 Pa

Page 149

The pressure of any liquid is the same in all directions and increases with depth, so dams must be built to withstand the greatest pressure at the bottom.

Page 150

1   Equals, pressure, closed, F_2/A_2, ten, pedal, same, pressure.

2   a   The pressure is the same throughout any closed system.

   b   The force on piston 2 is five times greater than the force on piston 1. This is because force/area is the same throughout the system, so if the area at piston 2 is five times bigger than at piston 1, the force must also be five times bigger.

Page 151

a   Longitudinal   b   Transverse

c   Transverse   d   Transverse

e   Longitudinal.

Page 152

300 000 000 m/s

Page 155

1   Refracted, normal, critical, reflected, total, reflection, from, to.

3   a   Periscope

   b   Optical fibre.

3   a   If the light hits the surface at greater than the critical angle, it will reflect from the surface, even though is not silvered.

   b   Total internal reflection bounces the light rays all the way along the fibre.

Page 158

a   i and ii

b   iii

c   ii.

Page 159

A   P-waves

B   P-waves

C   P and S-waves.

S-waves will not travel through the liquid core.

Page 161

Southern, axis, winter, summer, shorter.

Page 162

a $^{10}/_9$ = 1.1 N

b $^{10}/_{16}$ = 0.625 N

Page 163

Equator, same, poles.

Page 164

1   Nebulae (singular nebula)

2   a   The force of gravity pulls the gas towards the centre.

   b   The centre of the ball gets hotter as the gas particles convert their potential energy into heat energy.

Page 165

Nuclear, light, sound, solar.

Page 166 (top)

The particles in a gas are far apart so it would be difficult to transfer vibrations through it.

Page 166 (middle)

In conduction the material through which heat is travelling doesn't itself move. In convection the actual material moves.

Page 167 (top)

1   The black beaker would cool faster. It would radiate the heat away faster than the silver beaker. This is another way of saying that the silver beaker would reflect the heat back into the beaker.

2   Shiny, reflected, electromagnetic, worse, good.

Page 167 (middle)

As we burn more fossil fuels we produce more carbon dioxide. Carbon dioxide is a greenhouse gas which means it prevents the escape of some of the heat from the Earth. It allows short-wave infrared radiation from the Sun through to the Earth. This heats up materials of the Earth which become hotter than their surroundings. These radiate heat of a longer wavelength. The carbon dioxide does not allow this infrared of a longer wavelength to escape.

Page 168 (top)

1   Hotter, slow, air, layers, air, better, insulator, convection.

2   The vacuum between the double walls of the flask prevents heat loss by convection and conduction. The stopper prevents heat loss by evaporation. Glass is a good insulator and the silvering reflects heat back into the flask.

Page 168 (bottom)

1   Chemical energy (from fuel)

   $\rightarrow$ kinetic energy of the moving car. (Some is converted to electrical energy to charge the battery.) Energy is lost as heat and sound.

2   33.33%

Page 169

1   2000 J. (Did you remember to change the mass to weight? 100 kg has a weight of 100 x 10 N.)

2   40 watts (120 kg x 10 N/kg x 2m/60 s) (Did you remember to: a Find the weight of the sugar in newtons, b Convert the time into seconds?)

Page 170

3000 N

Answers

    1   Beta radiation would be used. Alpha would not pass through the aluminium tin, gamma would pass through the beans and the tin, but beta would be stopped by the combination of aluminium and beans and would give a change in reading if there were not enough beans in the tin. A long half-life would be best to avoid frequent replacement of the source.

    2   a   Gamma (good penetration is needed so it can be detected at a distance)

          b   Fairly short – long enough to be detectable, but not so long that contamination is caused.

    18 000 years (3 half-lives)